JESSE ELLIS

AND THE MAIDSTONE WAGONS

Frontispiece: Jesse Ellis (1846-1916) at the age of fifty-three.

R. A. Whitehead

JESSE ELLIS

AND THE MAIDSTONE WAGONS

An account of a pioneer builder of steam road wagons

R. A. Whitehead & Partners

Tonbridge, Kent.

1992

Published by R. A. Whitehead & Partners
42, Hadlow Road,
Tonbridge, Kent   TN9 1NZ

Front cover picture: Wagon No. 6 (1901) on demonstration to Mr. S. P. Sanders of Maidstone.

Photographs: The author acknowledges, with grateful thanks, permission to use illustrations as follows:- Cover, G. H. (Bobbie) King; Fig 2, Mrs E. O'Driscoll; Fig 10, Cadbury-Schweppes; Figs 11,12, Maidstone Borough Museum; Figs 13,14,15,16,17,18, *Engineering*; Figs 16,34,43,46,47,49, Museum of English Rural Life, Reading; Fig 44, National Motor Museum, Beaulieu; Fig 50, A. C. Coster.

Typeset by J. E. Whitehead.

Cover and title page set by J. N. King.

Printed and bound by Biddles Ltd., Woodbridge Park, Guildford, GU1 1DA.

ISBN 0-9508298-1-1

Contents

Foreword

by C.E.NORTH, B.Sc.,M.I.Mech.E.

The invitation to write this Foreword has given me great pleasure because firstly my family is old-established in Kent, and myself having been a resident for many years, the place-names and those of many of the firms covered in the book are familiar. Secondly, the subject matter has always been close to my heart. Having been brought up in farm and estate life when steam ploughing and threshing engines and road rollers abounded, steam has always fascinated me. However, I must admit that my main interest has been stationary engines although I claim to have learned to drive on a steam roller and now, as a septuagenarian, have graduated to firing steam wagons!

The almost complete disappearance in this country of steam in its reciprocating form during the middle part of the present century has meant that today people, both young and not so young, have little knowledge of the then everyday use of steam in industry, on the railways, on the water, on the land, and on the roads.

While interest in railways, which have always had a romantic image, is kept alive by preservation societies and by publications often in great detail, other aspects of steam usage risk falling into unrecorded history. An example is the steam road wagon which was the work-horse for early road transport of goods. Again, while the names of some better known makers may still be recollected, others, often located in small towns, can fall into oblivion. A case in point is Jesse Ellis of Maidstone, Kent.

While any historical account must be accurate in respect of events and dates, a complete narrative requires the author to be a specialist in his subject so that a living picture can be portrayed by a full explanation of developments including successes and inevitable frustrations.

The designer and builder of steam road vehicles did not possess the design aids of today and modern technology did not exist. Instead he would have relied on simple sketches and drawings together with rule-of-thumb and trial and error methods. Nevertheless the results would be essentially practical and often display great ingenuity.

In addition to being an engineer first and foremost, it is evident that Jesse Ellis needed also to be a manager and accountant, assessing commercial risks, as well as a salesman covering home and abroad.

The book gives an insight into employment of the workpeople. Life cannot have been easy and crews on the road would have needed to be stalwarts, every journey being somewhat of an adventure. Loyalty and discipline would have been demanded but fairness and friendship created a close-knit relationship.

This foreword attempts to set the scene for a praiseworthy and comprehensive account of an enterprising firm's wagon building and other activities and generally to stimulate the interest of the reader into the use of steam on the roads of yesteryear so that those wagons which still exist, preserved in caring hands, can be a source of enjoyment to a wider circle of so-minded people.

Charles North

Eythorne,
Dover.
February, 1992

Preface

Jesse Ellis is a neglected figure in the history of haulage by road both in his capacity as a haulier, *per se,* and in his work as a pioneer manufacturer of steam wagons. Besides these two activities he was a contractor for steam threshing, ploughing and sawing; a quarry owner; a supplier of agricultural machines, manures and insecticides; and a contractor, on a considerable scale, for road repair and construction.

Notwithstanding such a teeming business life he also found time to be a prominent figure in Freemasonry, and a long-standing member of the Volunteer Movement. Direct participation in politics he appears to have eschewed but he took a leading part in organising engine owners in local and national associations to resist the legal disabilities imposed upon the use of steam on roads.

Though his own schooling had been basic and brief, he was a champion of education and saw to it that his eight children attended good schools, insisting that his five daughters should be equally treated in this respect at a time when this was considered by many to be a pointless extravagance.

The idea of writing about him came first, in 1966, from the late Prince Marshall, when he was editor of the much lamented magazine *OLD MOTOR.* Prince was a loyal publisher and a valued, though sometimes exasperating, friend. He also had a good appreciation of the part played in pioneering heavy road vehicles by those early makers who, in the end, failed to establish enduring businesses or to receive public acclaim.

The information contained in this book has been gathered over a period of about twenty-five years and large numbers of people have given help, often on a very generous scale. A list follows of those who have contributed, in which I have tried to set out all of their names but inevitably, I fear, some will have been omitted, such is the fallibility of memory, so that it is necessary for me to crave here the forgiveness of any whose names I have failed to include. To all, whether mentioned or not, I extend my sincerest thanks.

Robert A.Whitehead

Tonbridge,
Kent.
28th January, 1992.

Acknowledgements and Thanks

Grateful thanks are due to Charles North for so kindly agreeing to contribute the foreword.

The researches upon which this book is based took place between 1966 and 1992, the greatest concentration in 1966-1967 and again in 1990-1992 with a quieter period in between, taken up by various projects, many of which produced as a by-product snippets of information about Jesse Ellis. Consequently to thank everyone concerned requires quite a large amount of space.

I should, perhaps, begin by mentioning how much I owe to G.H.(Bobbie) King, a longtime resident of Maidstone, deeply versed in its commercial and social life. Bobbie was the means of my meeting a number of interesting people. Through him I was introduced to Mrs Gwen Bramwells, grand-daughter of Jesse Ellis, and by her to her aunt, Mabel White, a daughter of Jesse Ellis, a redoubtable and witty old lady of great charm. Many other doors were opened to my enquiries by Bobbie's efforts but none gave quite the pleasure that my wife and I enjoyed by going to tea with Mabel White at Broadstairs on various occasions. Mrs White was the widow of J.Carter White, the petroleum technologist. In correspondence and also over tea at Broadstairs she gave us an amusing account of Maidstone at the turn of the century, and a great deal of anecdotal information on life in her father's household, on the men who worked for him, and of her journey with him to Egypt in the autumn of 1902.

It was Bobbie, too, who arranged that we should meet Douglas Gray and Herbert (Bert) Standen of Fremlin Brothers' Brewery, the former the transport Manager, the latter the doyen of the office staff and for long the confidential assistant of the Board of Directors. Bobbie located also the whereabouts of the late W.A.Gowan, the nonagenarian and sole survivor, even in 1966-7, of the Jesse Ellis office staff. Mr.Gowan verified from personal knowledge a number of details that could otherwise only have been conjectured.

Edwin Pratt Boorman, head of the *Kent Messenger* group of companies, was of great assistance, allowing us the freedom of his papers' archives and those taken over from the *South Eastern Gazette*. We are also grateful to his ever helpful staff.

Mr.L.A.Mitchell and Mr.Bernard Thomas of the now disbanded motor registration department of the Kent County Council gave a great deal of help as did the staffs of the Maidstone Museum, the County Archivist and the County Library Service, particularly the Reference Library staffs at Maidstone and Tunbridge Wells.

As in many other things we have undertaken we have received much help from the Museum of English Rural Life at Reading, and the National Motor Museum at Beaulieu. At the former we would like to single out Jonathan Brown, John Creasey, and the late David Phillips, and at the latter, Lynda Springate, the present librarian, and her predecessors, Peter Brockes, Nick Georgano, and Eric Bellamy. Much assistance was received from the Institute of Mechanical Engineers, especially from Bill Brown of the Library. We also received help from the staffs of the House of Lords Records Office and of the Public Records Offices at Kew and Chancery Lane.

The late Derek Stoyel was a friend for many years and we had discussed making this book a joint project, an idea that came to an untimely end with his death in 1989. His son, Alan, who inherited his vast photographic collection, has, however, done everything possible to help. The late Tom Paisley also took a great interest in it in the initial stages, again an involvement abruptly cut short by his death. Alan Duke has given unstinted help from his engine records. Bill Love and his late father, William Samuel Love, provided interesting information. Mr.Love (sen.) had known not only Jesse Ellis but also his father George Ellis.

The staff of Trebor-Bassett at Maidstone and of the parent group Cadbury Schweppes went to great pains to locate for us the plans of the Invicta Works site as it was when taken over by their predecessor Edward Sharp. In particular, we would like to thank Mr.G.E.Briggs of the Property Office at Bournville.

Three former drivers helped with recollections of Ellis wagons, Charles Hooker, who at one time drove one for his father, Wally Cruttenden, who drove a Fremlin-owned example, and Arthur McCaffery, who worked for Style & Winch at the time they were working an Ellis wagon. Charles and Arthur are both dead and we have lost touch with Wally, but their recollections were all of great interest.

David Scotney and Bobbie King each provided information on the Headcorn & Maidstone Junction Light Railway and the Sutton Valence & the Maidstone Motor Omnibus Co.Ltd.

Other people who helped with various information were, in chronological order:- John Butler; Mrs Joan Landry; Geoffrey Fletcher; the late Arthur Wedgwood; the late Frank Lambert; Lou Humphrey; Harold Ellis (nephew of Jesse); Alan Day; Brian Thompson; David Fletcher; Mrs.Elizabeth O'Driscoll.

Our son-in-law, Michael Walters, not only helped to locate information but also read and commented upon the manuscript, as also did John Boughton.

In case any reader of these notes should imagine that use has been made of the "royal we" it should be explained that the other half of the "we" is my wife Jean. I must say how much the enterprise owes to her, my companion in forays into archives, commenter on phraseology and syntax, and indefatigable transcriber of my scrawled draft into type.

Sincerest thanks are extended to all these people, coupled with regret that many have not lived to see the book in print.

Fig 1: A view across the Medway of Sufferance Wharf and Invicta Works, c.1897, taken from the top of Fremlin's Brewery on the East Bank.

Fig 2: No 23 Union Street, Maidstone, c.1913.

Fig 3: Reconstruction of the Embankment roadway, Westminster, by Jesse Ellis & Co, 1895.

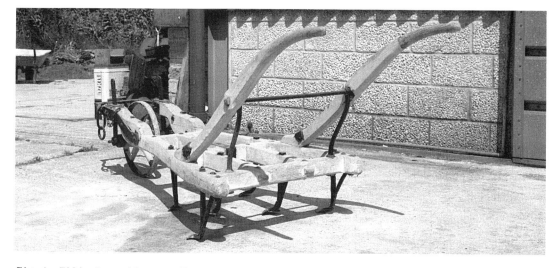

Fig 4: Ellis hop-nidget at Brattles Farm Museum.

Chapter 1

JESSE ELLIS -THE FIRST HALF HUNDRED

When Jesse Ellis was born on April 14, 1846, his parents lived in the parish of Cranbrook, Kent, but later his father, George Ellis, moved to a farm at Kippings Cross, Matfield, on the present A21 road, adjacent to the north-west quadrant of the roundabout at the junction of the Pembury by-pass with the old course of the road. From this address he carried on business as a threshing and sawing contractor, latterly using an Aveling & Porter 6NHP single cylinder traction engine No.690 built in 1871. The late William Samuel Love remembered George as, it seemed to him, a very old man who gave up the business about the turn of the century. The old engine and thresher were bought by W.Arnold & Sons of Branbridges, East Peckham. The portable saw-bench was bought by William Love's father who was a wheelwright and coach builder.

Jesse has been described as having been educated "at local schools". As he had finished with schooling long before the days of compulsory education it is likely that such formal education as he received was not extensive. Nevertheless he was far from illiterate and had, in addition, a good head for figures though it was his daughter's opinion that these attainments owed more to his own effort than to those of his educators. He was brought up amidst agricultural machinery and steam engines and it has been recorded that by the age of nine he was capable of running a portable steam engine single handed.

For a while after finishing with school Jesse worked for his father at the Baltic Saw Mill in Maidstone, but when he was eighteen he went to Thomas Aveling's works at Rochester for five years. His status there is not clear but obviously, from subsequent events, it brought him into much closer personal contact with the senior partner than would have been the case with an ordinary trade apprentice. From then onward he seems to have been on terms of friendship with Thomas Aveling and Richard Porter and later with Aveling's son, Thomas Lake Aveling. Credit from Aveling & Porter enabled him to set himself up at the age of twenty-three as a threshing, sawing, and haulage contractor. No doubt also it was whilst he was at Rochester that he met George Batey whom he was later to appoint foreman of his works at 23 Union Street, Maidstone, not far from the County Jail, now the site of County Hall. His marriage to Mary, daughter of John Moseley, of Yalding, gave them eight children - three sons, Jesse, Arthur, and Douglas, and five daughters, Daisy, May, Mabel, Millicent, and Edith, of whom only Jesse (b.1875), Mabel (b.1879), and May (b.1886) had any part in his business. The Ellis family home was on the Union Street frontage and a large pair of iron gates closed off the entrance to the yard. Mabel, who was born in the house, recalled how she and the other children had loved living there with the workmen in the yard to talk to and engines coming and going from time to time which they could watch.

Jesse's energy and ability were noted by Arthur Fremlin, one of the partners in the well-known Maidstone brewery not far away in Earl Street. In 1873, when Jesse Ellis was twenty-seven years old, he and Fremlin entered into a partnership as Jesse Ellis & Co. for a term of twenty-one years, to continue the business established by Jesse in Union Street and at Allington which had grown to include steam ploughing in its activities and needed additional capital for expansion.

It was the mutual misfortune of the new partners that after the firm had been in operation for three months Arthur Fremlin died, leaving his share to his widow, Marianne, who elected to retain it. It was fortunate in many ways for Jesse Ellis that she chose to remain a partner, thereby sparing him the onerous task of either buying out her share or finding a new partner to buy it from her but there was, on the other hand, the disadvantage that for the duration of the partnership he had to take upon his own shoulders the whole burden of management without recourse to the advice and commercial acumen of the older man for whose judgement he had had considerable respect. Though

Jesse made a point of consulting Mrs Fremlin on any decisions of moment, she took no part in the day to day management of the company which was left entirely to him.

Notwithstanding this upheaval the business flourished. By 1880 the engines it owned included a 6NHP traction engine, two 8NHP traction engines, four 8NHP road locomotives and three pairs of ploughing engines of 8, 12 and 14NHP respectively. All had been supplied by Aveling & Porter Ltd. of Rochester and all were single cylindered. Of these the oldest was one of the 8NHP traction engines which dated from 1867. The remainder had all been built since 1870.

To have progressed so far in so short a time and from such beginnings required a high degree of self-confidence and, perhaps, self-esteem. Had it not been for his inherent toughness and soundness of judgment he could scarcely have achieved so much. All this notwithstanding, his long-running record of success had a setback in 1880. During the night of December 2/3, one of his 8NHP engines, just over three years old, suffered a boiler explosion in Maidstone, killing one of its crew, in circumstances that reflected little credit on its owner's methods of management. The details of the incident are narrated in Chapter 5. Jesse was not at home on that night, having gone to Oxford late in the evening of December 2 in order to attend an auction the next morning. Mary Ellis telegraphed the auctioneer's office with the news so that his opening announcement at the sale was to the effect that an engine owned by Mr. Jesse Ellis had exploded in Maidstone during the night and if the owner was present in the gathering would he please return at once to Maidstone!

The explosion was the consequence of an incompetently executed repair to a crack in the firebox of the engine having been compounded by the safety valves having become inactive, for reasons never established beyond doubt. Jesse Ellis brazened or bluffed his way through his evidence at the adjourned inquest and escaped with no more than criticism by the coroner or the jury but had he not been appearing before a coroner who was one of the solicitors of the town and a jury of his fellow burgesses the outcome might easily have been more damaging to him than, in fact, it was.

According to Mabel White the explosion had a profound effect upon her father's habits of thought, as he instituted drastic reforms in his methods of management and repair of engines,in consequence of which the space available at Union Street was too cramped to accommodate both these changes and the continuing growth of the business. In 1885 the firm was moved to fresh premises in St.Peters Street, West Borough, that part of old Maidstone west of the Medway. The new site had a substantial frontage onto the river and also a small barge dock. This river traffic facility was known as Sufferance Wharf. The remainder was given the name of Invicta Works, previously used for the Allington establishment.

The 1880's saw a growing pressure upon road authorities to improve the surfaces of roads. Probably the spearhead of this movement was made up of those members of the rate-paying classes who had taken up cycling as a hobby, cycling having become a popular pastime by the mid-eighties. Many cyclists belonged to the Road Improvement Association whose energetic secretary, William Rees-Jefferies, was a well-informed and active advocate of better surfaces. Consequently the improvement of roads was a subject that came up frequently before local politicians and administrators who, in other times, would probably have been glad to leave it dormant. Moreover most of the turnpike trusts had foundered by the 1870's, leaving their roads as the responsibility of the Justices of the Peace for the county who, frequently having no labour force of their own, often turned to contractors to carry out their work. As the volume of such work increased Jesse Ellis took up road contracting with marked success. The organisation and supervision of these main road works were put on a more substantial footing with the setting up of county councils by the Local Government Act, 1888, which increased the work available to contractors still further and Jesse Ellis was able to secure a useful proportion of it for his firm. For a period of fifteen years he was responsible, for instance, for the maintenance of the main road from Maidstone to Folkestone besides work for other authorities. There were 592 miles of main roads in Kent under the control of the County Council, all maintained by contract except for the 136 miles in the East Kent division, which were looked after by directly employed labour. Kent County Council, on

2

the whole, adopted a progressive stance on road improvements. In the year 1892 -93 the average expenditure was £159-15-0 per mile (£159.75) or a sum approaching £95,000 for the whole mileage so it will be seen that in an age where a man might live in some style and keep a carriage on £600 a year there was a large sum open to tenders in road maintenance. Launching further afield from Kent he secured contracts for road works from the London Vestries. A contract of which he was especially proud was that for the renewal of the roadway of the Victoria Embankment in Westminster, undertaken in 1895. As an adjunct to his activities as a contractor for road works Jesse Ellis had ragstone quarries at Boughton Monchelsea, providing ragstone for use in his own operations as a contractor and also for sale to other firms or to road authorities. The Boughton ragstone was also brought down to Suffrance Wharf and transhipped there on to barges.

Besides the road works contracting and his involvement with the farming community as a steam threshing and sawing contractor Jesse Ellis also traded as a supplier of agricultural machinery, particularly tools for the hop-growing industry of Kent and the adjoining areas of Sussex and Surrey. He designed and patented his own type of share for the nidgets (cultivators) used for cultivating between the hills of hop gardens. In a related activity he acted as a supplier of quassia chips to hop farmers. The wood of a South American evergreen tree *Quassia amara* when reduced to small chips and steeped in water yielded a bitter tasting infusion used by hop growers to combat the attack of aphids on their hop bines. The wood was imported into the London docks in logs and taken by barge to Sufferance Wharf where it was reduced to chips in a machine of Ellis's own design. The brick built 'Quassia shed' can be seen in the back-ground of some of the pictures of the works.

In an age when few foods were immune to adulteration beer was not an exception. Certain brewers whose acumen was more developed than their integrity seized upon quassia as a cheaper, albeit much inferior, substitute for hops in the bittering of beer though none did so, as far as is known, in the hop-growing districts where Jesse Ellis found his markets for quassia.

Other products for hop farmers handled by Jesse Ellis & Co included manures in diverse forms and sulphur for dusting onto the growing plants as a palliative for the destructive disease of wilt. The enormous numbers of horses used in London produced a correspondingly great weight of stable manure that, in turn, led to a considerable commerce devoted to its disposal. A stable of 200 bus horses generated about a thousand tons of dung a year. When it is considered that there were probably some 350 000 horses of all types in London in the 1880's it will be realised how large the total tonnage was. Even after allowing for the fact that not all of the 350 000 were of the stature of bus horses the resultant weight of manure must have been of the order of 1¼ to 1½ million tons to which had to be added that which arose from the numerous urban cow-sheds where cows were kept to supply London with milk. Much horse dung was sent by train to rural stations and distributed by traction engines and trucks. Some was moved by barge but at the country end traction engines again were involved in moving it to its final destination. Jesse Ellis's company had a firm foothold in this traffic which, incidentally, was not nearly so noisome as the squeamish might imagine. Horse manure fetched about six to seven shillings (30 to 35 pence) a ton delivered on the farm and was in heavy demand by hop-growers.

The 80's and 90's of the last century saw arable farming in a state of intense depression. From over 14 million acres in 1880 arable fell to 12½ million in 1896, the ensuing reduction in the volume of threshing and ploughing resulting in keen pricing and much competition. Jesse Ellis who believed in taking no set-back lying down counter attacked in two ways. Firstly he took a leading role in the setting up of the Kent County Engine Owners Association in which he was associated with eleven other users of traction engines (J.Robson & Son, Henry Chapman, Walter Arnold & Sons, Chittenden & Simmonds Ltd, Thomas Wood & Son, S.Sladden, Church & Goodhew, W.Morris, Wingham Agricultural Implement Co, Sidney Neame, and Barmby & Wyles Ltd) and one traction engine maker (Aveling & Porter Ltd). The objective of the Association was to promote the interest of the members in such matters as resisting importunate demands by Local Authorities, railway companies or statutory bodies, agreeing on levels of wages and fixing minimum rates of hire. This latter would nowadays be illegal but was not in the 1880's. With subscription income of not much more than £25.00 a year the Association lacked the financial means to become an effective fighting force and though its active members met over lunch or dinner on a few occasions each year the only real effect of the deliberations was in price fixing and even there it possessed no sanctions to enforce the "Association rate".

The second way in which Jesse Ellis tackled the effects upon him of the agricultural depression was to canvass for heavy haulage work. Entering into this with his usual commitment he met with his customary success. In 1884 the Bath & West of England Agricultural Society, of which he was a member, held its annual show in Mote Park, Maidstone. Jesse undertook the haulage of the impedimentia of the show from the South Eastern Railway to the ground. His involvement, in fact, went much further and a great deal of the day to day liaison work between the show organisers and the town itself fell upon him. It seems they turned to him to find or provide whatever was needed. That the extent of his exertions was appreciated by his fellow burgesses and by the trade exhibitors at the show is demonstrated by the dinner they gave in his honour at Maidstone on Wednesday, January 14, 1885. There they presented him with an illuminated address on vellum, an inscribed silver salver of massive proportions, weighing 163 ounces, and a Copeland ware flower epergne, the salver and epergne each inscribed "Presented to Mr Jesse Ellis, as a mark of the high esteem in which he is held by his numerous friends...". The names of those numerous friends were written on vellum and handed to him with the framed address, the corners of the frame being carved respectively with a traction engine, a steam hammer, a square and compass, and a smith's arm, symbolising the branches of his business and, at least obliquely, his prominence in Freemasonry.

When the Royal Agricultural Society, of which he was also a member, held its show at Maidstone fifteen years later Jesse was on the local committee and on the executive of the railway committee. Already he had held for some years the cartage contract from the Midland Railway in respect of the Royal Show. The firm acted as haulage contractors for the South Eastern Railway in connection with the Maidstone Show. It moved, inter alia, 11 000 used railway sleepers from the station to the ground at Mote Park for use in the formation of temporary roads.

During the 80's a number of contracts for the haulage of Lancashire and Cornish boilers were undertaken. As the late Tom McTaggart remarked of heavy haulage firms in the preface to his book *The Iron Men of the Road* "had it not been for these boilers there would have been no need for most of the firms". The tribulations of the task of moving a group of such boilers from Oldham, Lancashire, to Millwall Docks, in London, were used by Jesse Ellis as illustrations of the vexations imposed upon road hauliers by highway and bridge authorities, when he submitted written evidence to the Select Committee of the House of Commons on the use of locomotives on common roads which issued its report on July 1, 1896. During this contract alone he had been summoned before magistrates on six separate occasions.

That he had been selected by his fellow engine owners as one of those to provide evidence on their joint behalf was a result of the energetic part he had taken in the formation of the National Traction Engine Owners' & Users' Association, which came formally into existence on December 6, 1893. The Kent County Association had been influential in setting up the meeting which brought the National Association into being; had booked Sadler's Wells Theatre, in London, to house the foundation meeting, and had persuaded the Member of Parliament for Tonbridge, Mr Arthur G.Boscawen, to take the chair. It had also succeeded in persuading most of the traction engine makers to attend the meeting. The importance that these latter attached to it can be judged by the calibre of their representatives - J.E.Ransome, Thomas Aveling, John McLaren, R.H.Fowler, Robert Eddison (also of the Fowler firm), Charles Burrell and Edwin Foden all went in person. Ambassadors were not deemed sufficient. Jesse was very prominent both in these activities and the subsequent affairs of the Association, but they are outside the scope of this book.

He also followed with interest the first beginnings of the motor car and attended as many as he could manage of the early motor trials in France and, later, this country, sensing that the creation of a class of motorists from amongst the wealthy and influential would create a further and powerful lobby for road improvement. He became member number fifteen of the Automobile Club (later to become the Royal Automobile Club) at its old address in 119 Piccadilly, London. Curiously, though, he never drove a motor car himself limiting his driving to traction engines, rollers and steam wagons.

Outside his business pursuits Jesse Ellis had two other private interests. The first was an absorbing devotion to Freemasonry, in which he was a member of no less than three lodges, the Montreal Royal Arch Chapter, the Robinson Lodge and the Robinson Mark Lodge. Of the two latter he was founder member.

The other was his active part in the volunteer West Kent Yeomanry Cavalry. He enrolled as a ranker though he soon became an NCO. By the eighteen-eighties he was given the non-commissioned rank of Farrier Quartermaster Sergeant, being barred by his sketchy education from a commission. The officers were almost a club of the younger members of the local landowning families and minor gentry to whom Jesse Ellis was invaluable because of his fund of practical experience. He was widely liked and his being a senior NCO enabled him to be invited to mix with the officers, nominally for consultative purposes, without protocol being offended. Altogether he gave more than 25 years service to the movement. When they ended, other changes were also afoot in his life.

Fig 5: A ploughing engine under the gantry in the open yard by the smiths' shop, Invicta Works. The open-sided "Smiths' Shed", containing one of the portables, is on the right of the picture.

Fig 6: A view down the East
yard at Invicta Works.
The distant building is
Fremlins Brewery.

Fig 7: The first buck-wagon.

Fig 8: The East yard at Invicta
Works, from near the front
entrance. On the left a
high-wheeled Aveling & Porter
road engine. The figure on the
manstand is said to have been
the legendary Tom Boarer.

Chapter 2

THE CLIMAX AND DECLINE

Jesse Ellis's collaborator in his latter enterprises was his eldest son. After early education at private schools in Maidstone from 1881 to 1890 followed by two years at Margate College Jesse (jun.) went on to an apprenticeship at Aveling & Porter's works at Rochester. It seems likely that his position there resembled more closely that of a pupil than of a trade apprentice as he returned with a good grounding in drawing and design and some experience of works management to become his father's understudy.

The two had a shared interest in the development of the motor car. Jesse Ellis often took his son with him on his visits to motoring events in France where they not only saw the burgeoning of the motor car but also of steam vehicles of large and heavier types. Jesse believed that the perfecting of a successful steam wagon as opposed to traction engines, was the means by which commercial traffic on roads might be developed, though as we have seen, he gave very active support to the efforts of the National Association to secure the liberalising of the law governing the use of traction engines.

So far as the home use of steam wagons was concerned he had his eye particularly upon the problems of Kentish farmers growing fruit for the London markets, who were profoundly dissatisfied with the railways as a means of transporting their fruit. None of the markets had rail connections so that the produce suffered a double trans-shipment - from road to rail at the country end and again rail to road in London. Even with careful handling and efficient management these would have been damaging hazards but the two railways serving Kent, the South Eastern and the London, Chatham & Dover, made poor scores for either care or efficiency, "take it or leave it" often summing up the treatment farmers received. Doubtless, therefore, Jesse felt that a wagon capable of running direct from farm to market would be a readily saleable product and that he, with his established connections with farmers, would be in an exceptionally favourable situation to sell such a vehicle.

In parallel with this, however, was another consideration, the nascent market in South Africa, where the oxen widely used as draught animals were falling victim to the destructive attacks of rinderpest and where, moreover, one of his partner's relations, A.G.W.Fremlin, was farming, thereby creating a direct link. This is discussed in more detail in Chapter 8. It was this project that father and son brought to completion first. Jesse Ellis took out a patent (No.11901 of May 13, 1897) for what he referred to as a "Colonial buck-wagon", a high wheeled steam lorry with the engine and vertical boiler at the rear. How long this took to build and where the actual building took place is not now clear. Mabel White believed that much of it was made at Invicta Works but the boiler, judging by subsequent practice, was probably bought in from a firm of specialist boilermakers, as must have been the iron and steel castings.

The twenty-one year partnership agreement with Mrs.Fremlin expired in 1896 but was continued for the time being by the consent of the partners. It is not known at what stage Jesse Ellis revealed to Mrs.Fremlin his analysis of the future of steam wagons and the business opportunity he saw in taking up their manufacture. At fifty he was still a dynamo of energy but his proposition, nevertheless, was a bold one. That he put his case convincingly is evidenced by Mrs. Fremlin agreeing to take part in the venture. Both were fairly well-off. The capital value of the business and the premises probably stood at about £2.5 million in terms of today's money besides which each of them had substantial assets elsewhere.

The expiration of the partnership, and the new direction in which it was proposed the business should strike out combined to make it appropriate to turn it into a limited liability company, both from the point of view of bringing in the necessary new capital and also of distancing the partners' private wealth from any additional hazards that might be introduced by the new products.

Whilst the discussions were under way in 1897 the affairs of the town and the firm were thrown into confusion by the Maidstone typhoid epidemic brought about by the pollution of the public water supply. For most of the summer there was no mains water and the inhabitants had to manage with water brought in carts from two pure springs at Otham. The cause of the outbreak was finally traced to the peculiar type of fire hydrants provided in the town in which internal water pressure kept the hydrant closed by pushing an india-rubber ball against a concave seat. If, as it regularly was at night, the water was turned off to save losses by leakage, the balls dropped off their seats. As the hydrant pits were often full of foul material or surface water the opening of the hydrant allowed this to enter the mains with the eventual result of the major outbreak of disease that happened in 1897. Nevertheless, despite these events progress was made with the reconstruction of the firm and the building of the prototype steam wagon. By the new year the former was nearing completion and on March 4, 1898, a new private company was registered under the title Jesse Ellis & Co.Ltd., the subscibers of which were Jesse Ellis himself, Frank and Fred Beadle of Dartford, Ralph and Frank Fremlin, Thomas Scott, a well-to-do farmer of Ditton Court, Maidstone, and Percy Burt, the company's solicitor. All these gentlemen became shareholders together with Marianne Fremlin, Thomas Lake Aveling, Richard Porter, various other members of the Fremlin, Ellis, and Beadle families, and a considerable number of tradesmen and townspeople of Maidstone and the North Kent towns. One outside shareholder, William Cable, a farm manager of Teston near Maidstone, had 500 shares whereas Thomas Lake Aveling and Richard Porter had bought only 250 each. To them, as wealthy men, £250.00, though probably in excess of £30 000.00 in todays currency, was a decent gesture of support to an old friend whereas to Cable it probably represented the outcome of a lifetime's savings. Robert Batcheller, the timber merchant, Ellis's neighbour in St.Peters Street, had 250 shares as did Abraham Flint, the corn and coal merchant at Larkfield. Of minor shareholders George Blackett, a salesman, and his wife Grace, of St.Michaels Terrace, Maidstone, had 10 and 15 shares respectively.

Of the authorised capital of £60 000.00, £33 165.00 was issued. The outgoing partners received £40 000.00 for the assets handed over to the new company, of which sum £17 707.00 was to be in cash, £10 000.00 in ordinary shares in the company and the balance in either cash or shares at the option of the new board. In the event most of this balance seems to have been taken in shares. In addition to the monies received from shareholders the Board created £15 000.00 worth of debentures in £50 units, by an instrument dated May 15, 1898. Thus, though the creation of the new company had released a substantial proportion of the partners' capital and had interposed the barrier of limited liability between their personal assets and the liabilities of the company, nevertheless they remained the majority shareholders by far.

Work on the wagon had been largely complete before the upset caused by the epidemic. The Royal Show had been destined to be held in Maidstone in 1898 but was hurriedly transferred to Birmingham and it was there, rather than in its native town, that the wagon was shown. Eventually the Royal did reach Maidstone in 1899 where two more were shown. Of these I was fortunate to receive an eye-witness account. They were seen by William Love, who already knew Jesse Ellis's father, George, and was, in consequence, very interested in what had been built by Jesse's firm. One wagon was undoubtedly an amended version of the colonial buck-wagon shown the previous year -of this a photograph survives. The other, which most caught the 20 year old William's attention, was a 2-ton vertical boilered undertype wagon, with the boiler at the front, the final drive by roller chains and bodywork offered as suitable for carrying fruit. The buck-wagons were to prove to be a dead-end. The 2-tonner, however, pointed the way in which the firm's future production of wagons and, indeed, to some extent, that of the whole wagon trade, was to go.

As a young man Jesse (jun.) suffered badly from asthma. By 1898 his health had reached a very low point. According to his sister Mabel, he was recommended to live for a while in a hot, dry climate for which reason he applied successfully for a post as a junior engineer with John Aird & Co, the contractors for the Nile Dam at Aswan in Upper Egypt, under John Blue, their Senior Engineer,beginning there in October, 1898. Almost at once he began to comment in his letters home on the potential for the use of steam wagons in Upper Egypt and the Sudan.

Soon afterwards his father visited him in Egypt, taking the opportunity to visit some of the ports and cities of the Eastern Mediterranean - Athens, Jaffa and Cairo - on his way. One assumes, with no positive proof, that at least part of his motive in undertaking the trip must have been to discuss the wagon project. This apart, however, Jesse (sen.) may well have felt that at fifty-two with a successful business behind him the time had come at which he could afford the luxury of such a voyage. His second visit to Egypt in 1902 is described in Chapter 11.

Early in 1903, Jesse Ellis (jun.), having completed his engagement in Egypt, returned to Maidstone to join his father's firm as work's manager and probably as design engineer also. Who had been responsible for design in his absence is a matter of speculation. Though Jesse Ellis himself knew what he wanted to build and the general methods he wished to utilise, all of those to whom I talked about the matter when doing my investigations in 1966 agreed that he would certainly not have had the time and probably neither the technical knowledge nor the patience to have spent days at the drawing board on detail work. W.A.Gowan, who was a clerk at Invicta Works from 1897 to 1901, recalled a Mr.Page coming to the works as a draughtsman and being installed in a separate office, whom he believed might have been responsible for the detailing of the early wagons. This view has weight added to it by the wording of Patent Application No.12675 (1899) filed in the joint name of J.F.Page and Jesse Ellis & Co. Ltd. This related to a system of engine hangers later to be the kicking-off point for a design incorporating a separate sub-frame. Nevertheless he (Gowan) was convinced, as was Mabel White and her niece, Gwen Bramwells, that Jesse Ellis (jun.) was responsible for all or most of the design of the wagons.

Whilst it was very hard to design a satisfactory wagon that complied with the 3-ton maximum unladen weight prescribed by the 1896 Act when this limit was raised to 5-tons after the Motor Car Act of 1903 much more was feasible. The development work on the wagons taken with the equipping of the works to build them had required more cash than was to hand and the company had raised the additional monies required by the issue of the debentures created in 1895. By April, 1901, the total of these was £12 450.00, the trustees being Richard Fremlin and Arthur Brabazon Urmston, a Maidstone solicitor. A further issue of shares, to the value of £2 650.00 was made in March,1904.

The financial prospects of the company came under pressure from changes in the other aspects of its trade as well as wagon building. Whilst the position of arable farming improved a little from the turn of the century onward, competition for the resultant threshing and ploughing work it afforded was also greater. Increased competition, too, cut the profits in the roller hiring section of the business. In particular the Eddison Steam Rolling Co. Ltd. of Dorchester, Dorset, undergoing a vigorous expansion under Joseph de Mattos, canvassed actively for work in Kent and London - areas in which Jesse Ellis had been most active. Worst of all, however, from his point of view was the tendency that developed in the first decade of this century for road authorities to set up effective direct labour forces, equipped with steam rollers and, in some cases, also with steam tractors and trucks to carry out the work previously let out to contractors. The loss of the work on the main roads of Kent to the County Council's own road department, conceived and set up by Henry Maybury during his term of office as County Surveyor (1904-1910) might have been compensated by an increased turn-over in other parts of the business but this did not happen. The steam wagon building continued to soak up cash resources in the preparation of new designs, while the agricultural contracting and roller hire sections stagnated if they did not actually regress. By the spring of 1906, though the board still believed the company to be solvent, it had become clear that a substantial part of the capital value was irretrievably lost. Consequently an Extraordinary General Meeting was convened at the Cannon Street Hotel on May 25, 1906, at which the value of each ordinary £1 share was written down to 10 shillings(50p).

Though this move helped to inject realism into the capital structure of the company, it did nothing to reassure its creditors but rather made the position more tense. Perhaps worse was the consequence that it caused the debenture holders to look askance at the security of the money they had advanced. Their apprehension had increased so much by the spring of 1907 that Richard Fremlin and Arthur Urmston, acting in their capacity of trustees for the debenture holders, entered into possession of the firm on April 18. William Day (jun.), a well-known Maidstone auctioneer and valuer, was appointed receiver. On April 30 another extraordinary general meeting was convened at the Cannon Street Hotel. This time there was no talk of reform and a resolution was passed that the company be wound up, Richard Crosby, the company secretary, being appointed liquidator.

From the date of the receivership most of the trading thereto carried on by the company ceased, though some of the contracting work in progress was brought to completion and wagons under construction in the works were finished to a saleable state. Everything capable of being realised was gathered in the works where it was sold in a three day sale on October 1, 2 and 3, 1907. The sale was widely advertised and attended by buyers drawn from all over the country. The prices fetched by the lots were said in the press reports to have been "very satisfactory" but no priced catalogues have been located so it is not now possible to verify this comment in detail. Though most of the plant and stock-in-trade was sold at the October sale, a number of items including at least two complete wagons and the steam bus (see Chapter12) remained unsold. The Receivership continued until December 27, 1912. A very large asset of the defunct company was the freehold of Invicta Works. Initially this was offered for sale by auction on July 10, 1907, but no bids were forthcoming and it remained in the hands of the Receiver who let it on short tenancies until October 7, 1912, when it was sold to Edward Sharp as a site for his confectionary works. Sharp abolished the dock and demolished most of the buildings but the office and manager's house survived until the 1970's.

Though the failure of the company must have been a grievous blow to Jesse Ellis and the cause of financial loss he was by no means a ruined man. In partnership with Richard Crosby he bought in a number of the engines at the dispersal sale (see Appendix III) and continued to trade as a roller owner and agricultural contractor, albeit on a reduced scale. He had also owned, independently of the company, Allington Forge, and he carried this on as a general agricultural engineering and blacksmithing establishment on the London Road just outside the town limits reviving its old name of Invicta Works. An advertisement for the reconstituted business appeared in the Kent Messenger Directory of Maidstone, 1909, drawn in the following terms:

JESSE ELLIS & CO
Steam ploughing, sawing, threshing, road rolling
Traction Engine Proprietors and General Engineers
Repairs done to all kinds of farm implements and machines
ALLINGTON WORKS, London Road, Maidstone
Contractors for the supply of road material and for the making
and maintenance of roads
Agents and brokers for any kind of new and second-hand machinery
Valuers of machinery

The Allington firm did not endure and the partnership was dissolved in 1910, the plant being sold by auction. According to Mabel White the forge business was sold to William Humphrey, Jesse Ellis retaining the freehold of the premises which were leased to Humphrey.

After this he amused himself for a year or so as an engine broker and valuer.In 1911, for instance, he successfully tendered a price of £76.00 for Penge U.D.C's superseded roller (A.&.P.No.2220 of 1885) which he sold in turn to W.Arnold & Sons at Branbridges. He moved from *Kingsgate* to a house called *Burnside* in Chestnut Road, West Norwood, Surrey. Jesse's health became very poor and he died there, at the age of seventy, on October 17, 1916. He was buried in Maidstone on October 21 after a service at St.Peter's Church at 1.15p.m. Up to the onset of his final illness he had continued to take an interest in the affairs of the National Traction Engine Owners Association, of which he was a Vice-President at the time of his death.

In not much more than a decade from the boiler explosion he had progressively shed the swashbuckling image he had created for himself in his youth until in his fifties he had become a pillar of the establishment. In 1898 when he was proposed by his friend, Charles D.Phillips, for associate membership of the Institution of Mechanical Engineers the seconder was Thomas Lake Aveling and the supporters were Robert Eddison (of John Fowler & Co.), Charles (jun.) and Frederick Burrell, J.E.Ransome and J.R.Jefferies. On the subject of boiler inspection and insurance he had undergone a conversion nearly as dramatic as St.Paul's on the road to Damascus. From being a scoffer at the time of the explosion he had become such a convinced advocate of both that by 1904 when he was put up for full membership of the Mechanicals by Thomas Lake Aveling, the first of the four seconders was C.E.Stromeyer, Chief Engineer of the Manchester Steam Users Association, a leading boiler inspection and insurance company.

Fig 9: A group outside Allington Forge c.1910. They are (l.to r.) Messrs.'Shrimpy' Waghorn (boilermaker), Jupp, George Bennett (foreman driver), and, reputedly, Tom Mason (jun.)

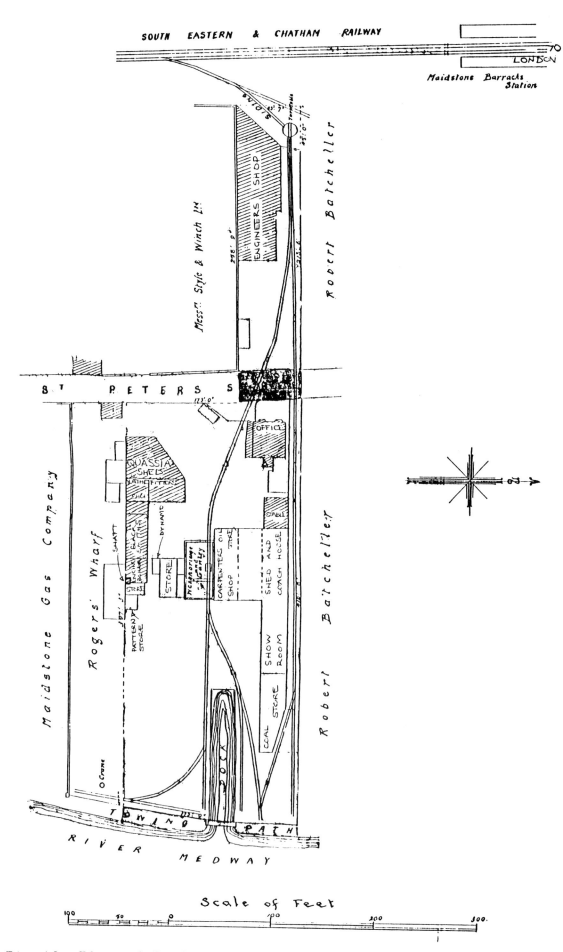

Fig 10: Plan of Invicta Works, c.1910.

Chapter 3

THE WORKS

The premises at 23 Union Street from which the business of Jesse Ellis & Co was carried on from 1869 to 1885 consisted of a dwelling house and office on the road frontage and, according to Mabel White, a yard at the rear with limited workshops, the approach to which was under an arch. She lived there only as a very young child and she was vague as to how the archway and boundary wall were arranged. Jesse also owned the forge and a yard at London Road, Allington, which he called Invicta Works. This land was personal property and not owned by the partnership.

The growth of the business made the Union Street site, with its awkward access from a street in the old part of the town, quite inadequate for its purpose. Furthermore, as has been noted, the 1880 boiler explosion brought about a pronounced change in the attitude of the managing partner towards systematic maintenance causing him to look for much larger premises where there would be room for more effective workshops.

The area in which he eventually found a suitable site was in that part of Maidstone known as West Borough on the west bank of the River Medway, a little to the north of St.Peters church. Though a nucleus of old houses already existed in the area immediately round the west approach to the road bridge over the Medway the area to the north of this along the river bank had remained meadow land until the late eighteen-seventies, when a new road (St.Peters Street) was built through it. In July, 1879, the plot of ground subsequently bought by Jesse Ellis was acquired by John Tomlyn, a timber merchant, who laid it out for use in his business. He constructed a barge dock, about 28 feet wide, penetrating some 275 feet into the site. In the north-west corner he built a works house and office and behind it, on the north and west sides of the dock, some sheds for storing timber. He also set up a lath rending workshop, a coach-house and two stables separated by a harness room.There was besides a small building called "the Cook House" though whether this cooked food for the workmen or mashes for the horses is not clear. This site extended just under 400 feet from the towpath back to St.Peters Street to which it had a frontage of 173 feet. Another and narrower piece of land, averaging about 64 feet wide and 268 feet long ran from St. Peters Street as far as the North Kent railway line of the South Eastern Railway, not far from the Maidstone Barracks Station. On this he built a substantial shed for "Contractors'Stores". These two pieces of land, together with rights over the strip of St.Peters Street which lay between them amounted to about two acres and were conveyed to Jesse Ellis and Marianne Fremlin in June 1885 at a cost of £2 660.00. The river frontage and dock Jesse Ellis called Sufferance Wharf and the remainder Invicta Works, supposedly at the same time dropping the use of that name for the Allington site.

The main purpose of Sufferance Wharf was, on the one hand, the unloading of sea-borne roadstones such as Scottish or Guernsey granite or Continental basalt and porphyry, and on the other, the loading of ragstone for shipment by barge mainly to the areas of what J.B.Earle has termed "the roadstone deficiency areas" of East Anglia. Kent ragstone, not all from Jesse Ellis's dock, was discharged at numerous small wharves and docks on the coast and estuaries of Essex and Suffolk. But besides this traffic in stone he also landed the considerable amount of coal used in his business and smaller lots of other types of goods. Quite a lot of the trade to Maidstone was still waterborne in the 1880's. The river traffic down stream had been made easier since the Lower Medway Navigation Company had improved the lock at Allington in 1880 and upstream, towards Tonbridge, since the opening of the new three span bridge in 1879 which had enabled the old structure of five spans, constrictive of waterborne traffic, to be cleared away.

Whereas the traffic at many of the older wharves in the town was handled by hand-worked derricks or cranes or simply, as in the case of bricks, manhandled, Jesse Ellis equipped his dock with a steam crane and a rail connection to the South Eastern

Railway near Maidstone Barracks Station. Jesse Ellis had his own ragstone quarries at Boughton Monchelsea, part of the output of which was shipped from Sufferance Wharf. Among the barges that loaded ragstone was the *Exchange*, owned by Thomas Adamson Riggs of Aldeburgh, the cargo destined to be landed at the Stone Wharf by Snape Bridge on the River Alde and used for the maintenance of the roads around Aldeburgh and Leiston. By coincidence not far upriver from Jesse Ellis's works, and on the opposite bank, were the premises of Balls Garrett, uncle of the two partners, Richard and Frank Garrett, then running Leiston Works as a manufactory of traction engines, portable engines and agricultural machines, whose products were sold, from time to time, by their uncle. In earlier days these, too, had been carried by barge but by the 1880's most were sent on the railway.

Jesse Ellis moved into the Works House for a while but subsequently bought himself a private house named *Scraces* at Barming. Later he moved to *Kingsgate* (now a hotel) in London Road, Maidstone. On the other side of the yard from the house, on the front of the old coach-house and stable, he put up a substantial brick building on two floors, splayed off on plan at the front, so as not to impede the works entrance. This was the Quassia Shed and housed the plant for making quassia chips as well as acting as a store for them. The coach-house itself became a fitters' shop and its stable a turnery or lathe shop. The harness room and the other stable, knocked into one, formed a blacksmiths' shop. On the east end of the existing building he erected an engine house and boiler room with a large brick chimney. These housed, respectively, a 10HP horizontal steam engine and a Cornish boiler which between them provided the power for the line shafting by which the machines were driven. East again of the engine house was a store which joined up with the former "Cook-house". This latter was made into a pattern store. The old coach-house and stables had formed an L-shape and the area bordered by this was roofed over to form "the Smiths' shed". On the east end of this was another store building with lean-tos on its north and south sides. The south lean-to eventually housed the 10HP Otto type gas engine and Stevens dynamo by means of which the works was lit by electricity. Jesse Ellis was a pioneer user of electric lighting some years before a public supply existed. The existing timber stores on the north side of the site were altered. The end nearest the river became a showroom for agricultural machinery and, later, the steam wagons. Part of the remainder became a coach-house and store, the balance a carpenters' shop and oil store. A smaller existing store between these buildings and the house garden was made into a stable and granary.

On the other side of St.Peters Street the long store was taken down and a substantial engineers' shop built nearer to the railway. Finally at the east end of the showroom and parallel with the side of the dock a large coal store was built into which coal from the coasting barges could be discharged. Besides the main engine the works, in its final form, also had a marine type compound engine and a three cylinder Brotherhood engine but where these stood or what supplied them with steam is not recorded. Also on the river side, on the south flank of the Invicta Works, was a second timber yard owned by a Mr.Rogers. This had another barge dock, a brick office noted as being 25 feet by 16 feet on plan, four sheds for timber and a 1-ton Scotch derrick for unloading. At a later date, not now known exactly, Jesse Ellis & Co. took over this yard on lease.

Almost as soon as the firm had taken possession of the new works Jesse Ellis began negotiations with the South Eastern Railway for a siding connection. The agreement for it was signed on March 22, 1886, authorising an end-on connection to a reverse siding from the down line just to the south of Maidstone Barracks Station. The levels were reasonably compatible and, after dividing, the line dropped down to a turntable on Jesse Ellis's property on which the wagons were turned through about 60° and discharged onto a short length of gauntletted track running past the new engineers' shop. About two-thirds of the way along it the tracks diverged, one continuing the whole length of the north boundary to a set of stops by the towpath. The other ran down diagonally to the centre of the main site about abreast of the quassia shed, passing, on its way, the south side of the house. It then continued down the centre of the site to the towpath, serving the south side of the dock. A branch ran down the north side of the dock, dividing by the west end of the dock and continuing as far as the towpath. A set of points and a connecting line to the siding along the north boundary provided a head-shunt. There was a line parallel with the river, beginning at the south wall of the dock and extending to the south boundary. This afterwards was extended onto Rogers' Wharf. It was connected to the line along the south wall of the dock by a link spur. This arrangement, being bereft of a head shunt, must have been more difficult to work than the lines on the north side of the dock.

The other line from the dividing point at the entrance to the site continued into the timber yard of his neighbour on the north side, Mr.J.S.Gabriel, who was later superseded by Robert Batcheller. The arrangements with Invicta Works involved two crossings on the level over St.Peters Street, originally, as has been noted, a private road, though subsequently adopted by the Borough Council. It joined up with Buckland Hill to the north to make a connection with London Road.

For working these tramways within the works Jesse Ellis bought a second-hand Aveling & Porter geared steam locomotive. Though the identity of this machine is not known for certain there are pointers that at least suggest its identity. In the first place it must have been on the market about 1886. The researches of Ian Hutchinson into Aveling geared locomotives, during which he recorded the successive owners and traced out the known careers of the various locomotives, have made it plain that No.1688 (1881) - the experimental double-ended tramway loco designed to incorporate Kingdon's Patent - is a probable candidate for the honour. It was in Aveling & Porter's hands at the relevant period. Jesse Ellis was a protégè of Thomas Aveling and was accorded the opportunity of buying useful second-hand engines taken back by their builder. From Jesse Ellis's point of view the tram engine was likely, being a failure for its intended purpose of traction on street tramways, to have been available cheaply, a telling consideration. It seems unlikely, however, that we shall ever know the loco's identity for certain. Besides the geared loco there was also a travelling steam crane of 3-tons capacity used mainly for cargo handling at the dock.

The area of yard between the smiths' shed and the carpenters' shop was provided with an overhead gantry and travelling crane. This was probably used when engines were being stripped for repair and when heavy items such as tubes, plates or complete boilers were to be taken off railway trucks. New engines invariably came home on their own wheels, usually with Jesse Ellis himself driving. It was as much a part of his personality as the bone-crushing handshake and the roaring geniality that all the things he expected his workmen to do on his behalf he would have been well able to do himself. When, for instance, he took the demonstration wagon to Egypt in 1902 it was he himself who drove it up the Citadel Hill to show what it could do.

A story used to circulate that he and his friend Walter Arnold felt that their noses had been put out of joint by their mutual and much younger acquaintance, Joseph de Mattos of the Eddison Steam Rolling Co, having tendered for and obtained the contract for roller hire of West Ashford Rural District Council. As a riposte to the young upstart they put in a successful bid for rolling work on *his* own doorstep and then drove the roller down to Dorset themselves. Both remained on perfectly good terms with the Rabelaisian de Mattos and Mabel White recalled her brother Jesse spending holidays with de Mattos and his wife in Dorset.

The equipment in the main shops at the time of the winding up included fifteen lathes, some equipped for screw cutting; shapers; planers; borers; screwing and milling machines; a punching machine; a 15cwt steam hammer and a face plate lathe to turn 6 feet diameter (supposedly for turning traction engine and roller wheels). Other items listed at the sale were a tyring platform, a set of 6 foot plate rolls and large quantities of stores and hand tools, together with wood working machines - sawbenches, morticers and a Fox's universal wood trimmer.

Whilst the firm undertook boiler repairs it did not, so far as one can tell, build complete new boilers. Certainly the boilers for the steam wagons were bought from outside builders, most of them probably from T.Balmforth & Co of the River Lea Boiler Works, Luton, Bedfordshire, but some also from Alfred Dodman & Co Ltd. of King's Lynn, Norfolk. The late Charles Hooker of Boughton Monchelsea was often in and about the works, sometimes with items for repair and at others with one or other of his father's traction engines bringing in wagon loads of ragstone for shipment at the wharf. Remembering the amount of plant in the boilersmiths' shop he was surprised that the building of the wagon boilers was put out. He did not recall there being a foundry at the works and with William Weeks & Sons having a good foundry opposite them on the east bank of the Medway it may have been deemed unnecessary. Nor must it be overlooked that a substantial proportion of the steam wagon castings were of steel, economically not readily adaptable to small scale production and most advantageously bought from a specialist foundry. The items noted in the auctioneer's abbreviated inventory on the sale posters do not include any foundry equipment and no foundry appears on the plans. These facts, taken with the other evidence, are sufficient, I think, for the existence of a foundry to be discounted.

During the final partnership with Richard Crosby from 1907 - 1910 the engine side of the business was housed at London Road, Allington, in a galvanised iron building 65 feet x 35 feet on plan. Amongst the plant installed were two 10" double geared screw cutting gap lathes, each with a 16 foot bed. The quassia chipping machine complete with its elevator and bagger was also taken there. Power was provided by a "Jack of all trades" oil engine. All this was sold when the engines were auctioned by William Day & Son in the winding-up sale on September 21, 1910.

Figs 11 (left) and 12 (right): Views, respectively inside the smiths' shop and the engineers' shop, Invicta Works. Lou Humphrey thought that the figure leaning on the double framed wagon under construction might have been Jim Springett.

Chapter 4

THE WORKMEN

The names of most of the many hundreds of men who must have been employed by Jesse Ellis & Co during the period of nearly thirty-five years covered by their trading have been largely lost. Undoubtedly many of those employed in the road construction part of the business were likely to have been casual labourers employed for only short periods at a time but as far as one can judge Jesse Ellis treated his drivers and workshop men as steadies employed on a regular footing and not taken on and stood off as trade fluctuated week by week. Lou Humphrey, the son of the William Humphrey who took over Allington Forge when Jesse Ellis sold it, recalled the instance of Tom Burden who worked for Ellis from the time the business was set up until it closed. On one occasion when his engine was under repair for a week he was not stood off. as he might have been on many firms, but instead was sent up to Allington Forge to do odd jobs. The translation from purposeful work to what he regarded as time-wasting did very little for a temper already choleric so that when he came to write up his time sheet he showed his displeasure (or, I suppose, ingratitude) by putting in under the heading 'Work Done' the words "buggering about" and appended the signature "R.Soles", an action that led to him being nicknamed "Dirty-name" thereafter. Reported to Jesse Ellis the incident merely made him laugh.

Another trusted driver of very long standing was Tom Boarer whose service began in 1877 in Union Street and endured for life. Mabel White thought that he died not long before the firm was wound up but I have not been able to verify that from other sources. Whilst still young Tom had lost a hand in some accident but this did not stop him from becoming a proficient, resourceful and very loyal traction engine driver and one of those involved in the heavy haulage work of the firm. These powerful virtues had an obverse in a very rough tongue. He was normally in charge of a high wheeled Aveling traction. Latterly, however, he is thought to have driven *Polly*, the 8HP road locomotive built in 1900 which was named after Jesse Ellis's wife, Mary, who was known as Polly. In the course of a life-time employed in a trade scrutinized with a peculiarly jaundiced eye by the police and magistrates he was in numerous scrapes with the law, one of which involved no less a person than the Chief Constable of Kent.

Tom and another old retainer, named Manktelow, had the misfortune, when in charge of two of the company's engines near *The Bull* at East Farleigh to encounter the Chief Constable being driven in his carriage. The coachman signalled them to stop whilst he took his horses past the engines. This he was quite entitled to do. Both drivers stopped but the engines had just ascended a hill and, with bright fires, promptly began to blow-off steam at the valves. Under the irrational provisions of the Locomotive Act this was an offence and the Chief Constable sent his man forward to instruct them to stop it. After a struggle Manktelow succeeded, probably because his engine had an injector. Tom Boarer, with only a pump, did not. Both, in consequence, were prosecuted. The case began as the Chief Constable versus Jesse Ellis & Co, but upon the magistrates indicating that they looked upon it as proven the firm sought and received permission for it to proceed as Jesse Ellis & Co versus the two drivers, both of whom were convicted and fined. Mabel White believed her father actually paid the fines and took the course that he did only because the bench had the habit of being more lenient toward drivers than employers. Many men in his situation would not have paid.

A third Thomas who served Jesse Ellis well was Tom Mason. How he began in his service is not recorded. He is remembered in the capacity of the foreman of Invicta Works, and as a noted and profane swearer. Jesse Ellis himself was recalled as prone to shouting and swearing though without malice. Perhaps Tom Mason modelled himself on what he saw as his master's example though, in any event, such behaviour was often the norm for those in minor authority at that time and not looked at askance. It fell to Tom Mason's lot to fix the piece-rates for what was done in the works, an aspect of his duties that probably brought him more into disfavour with the workmen than any other. Tom lived at Gladstone Road in the part of the town near the old Union Street works and crossed the Medway on his way home by the footbridge beside the High Level Bridge on the Maidstone East railway line. After an enforcement of a particularly stingy set of piece-rates a little coterie of the aggrieved lay in wait for him in the dark on the footbridge and held him by the wrists over the parapet, threatening to let go unless he recited the Lord's Prayer accurately. Tom passed the test and was hauled back. Lou Humphrey, who related the story, reckoned it was probably the only time in Tom's life that he prayed.

His son, another Thomas, also worked for Jesse Ellis and succeeded his father as works foreman in the terminal years of the firm though I have been unable to discover whether this followed upon the death or only the retirement of his father. Tom junior's reign was short, however, ending with the cessation of work at Invicta Works in the autumn of 1907,although it seems likely that Jesse Ellis found him a job at Allington Forge as a figure which Lou Humphrey thought to be him appeared on a photograph taken there. Others in the photograph are 'Shrimpy' Waghorn, formerly one of the boilersmiths at Invicta Works, and a man named Jupp, who had also worked there. The fourth man shown in that picture is George Bennett, the then foreman driver. Wally Cruttenden remembered a fitter named Mark Harman and another whose name was Creasey. A further name mentioned was Len Langley.

Most of the other names that survive from the obviously numerous register of workmen are those who drove or managed the engines.Their names crop up quite often in newspaper reports of proceedings before the magistrates, usually for making smoke or emitting steam from the valves. Fred Wood had the dubious honour of probably being the last man in the service of the company to be prosecuted (in April, 1907) for making smoke, and was fined £1.00 with 9s.0d. costs for the offence whilst driving a traction engine and three trucks through Maidstone. George Batey, whom Jesse Ellis recruited in mid-1878 from Chittenden & Knight, was an experienced man who had been working with engines since 1853 and who had spent eight years in the Aveling & Porter works at Rochester, three as a boiler shop foreman and some while besides in charge of the smiths' shop. He gave somewhat evasive evidence at the boiler explosion inquest (Chapter 5) that made it clear that his control over the boiler management and repairs, on which he might have been looked upon as expert,was rather sketchy. Whether or not this led to him disappearing from the scene afterwards is not clear from this distance of time. He certainly seems not to have been there by the time wagon building began. By contrast, Jim Springett, an Ellis driver not directly involved in the accident, gave his evidence to the inquest clearly and decisively. He was still working for the firm when it foundered. Mabel White described him as a very capable and reliable man. Lou Humphrey, rather younger than Mrs.White, knew him only as an old man whom he described as a decent old sort. Arthur McCaffery recalled a driver named Sam Freed who transferred to Style & Winch at the Medway Brewery as a wagon driver when Invicta Works closed.

Another driver who enjoyed Jesse Ellis's confidence was Offen, who featured in many of the surviving pictures of steam wagons. It was he who was selected to be the driver of the wagon hired to the War Department to take part in the transfer of the equipment of the Artists' Rifles from Newhaven, Sussex, back to their depot in Duke Street, St.Pancras, after their annual camp in August, 1904. The *South Eastern Gazette* sent a reporter to travel with the wagon to London.

After a tedious journey by rail from Maidstone West to Newhaven he was given a place in a tent, only to be roused at 4a.m. to witness the cleaning and preparation of the wagon. At 6.35 the work of the day began. From then until 11.45 it was used to take loads from the camp to the station for loading onto the train. Once that was done it was loaded and sheeted down. Our reporter takes up the story:

When the tarpaulin was strapped on, it looked for all the world like a huge haystack.All being now ready save one last piece of luggage, a grave difficulty arose, grave for me, at any rate, because I happened to be that last piece, and the difficulty was where I should be stowed. There was not room on the driving seat, and

it was impossible to sit behind, as the tailboard was already filled. The top was 20 feet above ground, and that position was not inviting. There was only one place left. Both the coke bunkers were full, but by putting another sack of coke on top of the right hand bunker I could just manage to nestle alongside the smoke stack! After filling the tanks up, we left camp at five minutes to one, with a journey of sixty-four miles before us. In Newhaven itself 3 cwt. of coke was taken up and then we started our climb to Lewes. Facing gradients "like the sides of houses", we passed the village of Southease on the right at 1.30p.m. The roads were bad, the soft, yielding surfaces being covered with loose flint stones, but our powerful engine, with indignant snorts at the steepest gradients, continued to mount them with ease. Incline after incline we covered safely, thanks to the careful driving of Offen, and after many twists and turns in the road, if road it might be called, we stopped at the Abergavenny Arms at Rodmell in order to clinker out the fires and oil up. At eleven minutes past the hour our journey was resumed, but alas! the route, if it were possible, got worse and worse. Passing Iford on our right, we continued grinding up the eternal hills surely, though somewhat slowly, with our huge burden. At last, on reaching the brow of an extra "teaser" we sighted Lewes lying in a small valley below us. What we gained in the gradient, however, we were destined to lose in the curves of the road. Twisting at sharp angles almost every 100 yards, and sliding about on the loose flints, we were at last cleverly steered into the town. By this time the weather had become very dull and threatening, and when we entered the capital of Sussex shortly before three there was every promise of a wet day. Offen, with his usual caution and foresight, took every opportunity to keep his tanks well filled as he did not know the road. Accordingly we stopped three minutes in Lewes to fill from a water trough. The town itself, in the matter of winding streets, proved worse than the approach, but driving at a snail's pace we managed to safely negotiate all the corners. Although it was not "plain sailing", we had passed over the very worst part of our journey, and it is a matter for congratulation both to the makers themselves and to the men who drove the engine that we successfully climbed the gradients, and that, safe and sound, we halted in Cooksbridge for 15 minutes. The roads now, though far from good, were considerably better, but patches of hard and soft surface caused some variation in the running of the engine. This state of things did not last long, for the roads again presented soft cut up surfaces, and the gradients became more acute. When Sheffield Park lay two miles behind us, an amusing incident happened. Just ahead, an old lady driving a pair horse closed wagonette, rounded a bend. She looked at us with a fighting expression on her face, and kept resolutely in the middle of the road. The steersman drew to one side, but, of course, she could not pass while in the middle of the thoroughfare. She stopped, and we stopped. The position was becoming tiresome when a deep growl came from the driver's throat. This let loose the tongue of the old lady, who drawing to one side and passing, exclaimed "Ah, all right, all right! you'll come to a wrong end soon, you - you blooming haystack on wheels!"
Nothing of great interest happened until 6.35p.m. when we bowled into Forest Row. There a halt was made for the refreshment of the inner man.
The weather had improved, and the sun shone with considerable warmth, but the roads were no better.
It was nine minutes to eight when we started on our way again, with daylight showing signs of dying. The scenery all along this road is beautiful in the extreme, but after passing Forest Row (another long uphill gradient by the way) it is lovelier still, thick, sweet smelling woods on either side, and broad, flat plateaux of bracken and heather alternating. Climbing and climbing on, we sighted the fine old tower of East Grinstead church at a quarter past eight, and a little later entered the town itself. It being Saturday evening there were many people in the streets, and they gazed in astonishment as our towering load rolled majestically through. Even the local section of the Salvation Army Band paused in its exertions for a moment in order to gape at us! We left the town as we had entered it - up a steep hill.
Reaching the outskirts of East Grinstead at 8.30, a halt was made in order to light up the lamps as twilight was rapidly closing in. With it came the chill night air, and

although somewhat irksome during the day,the heat from the boiler through the night hours proved very comforting, despite occasional sulphurous fumes.

At three minutes to nine we stopped two miles outside East Grinstead for ten minutes to refill the tanks. By this time it had become almost dark, and to me at any rate the best part of our journey had commenced. Running evenly and smoothly on better roads, we passed uphill and down, and through thick woods, the forelights casting weird, fantastic shadows on the trees as we passed by. Ever and anon as Offen lifted the "flue-lid" to replenish the fires, the fierce red light shone upon us in the dark, lighting up our figures and giving us the appearance of demons "holding orgy" around a hissing cauldron.

On we went with steady throb, throb, the purring engine beating a quick tattoo to the flying trees and hedges, until presently the lights of Godstone station were seen, and at 10.57 we were making merrily for Croydon. At 11.30 Warlingham passed into the background, and twenty minutes later Kingsley followed. Now, however, we began to experience our first trouble - the tail light refused to do its task, persistently objecting to illuminate our number and the outer darkness for more than two or three minutes at a time. So seriously did this begin to delay, that eventually we had to tell off one to sit behind and hold the lamp with its number plate attachment, taking care that the lamp maintained a flame. Later on we bowled away at a good speed over the Purley tram track. Passing through Croydon, we did not stop again until entering the confines of Streatham.

Sleepy and worn out, we rolled down Brixton Hill, over Westminster Bridge, and finally reached the depot in Duke's Road, at a quarter past three - a run of 64 miles in 14½ hours, without, barring the lamp, a single mishap - a very, very creditable performance especially when the difficulty of the road and heavy freightage are taken into consideration.

Offen and his mate had by then been up and about for some twenty-three and a quarter hours, after a poor night. Not much had changed, perhaps, from the days of the boiler explosion in 1880 when Moses Martin, the driver of the engine concerned had worked a twelve hour day until 6.30 in the evening and had gone on again at midnight with the intention of working through until 8a.m.

Also in evidence in steam wagon days was Tom Town who lived at Havock Lane. No one now remembers, nor did they in 1966, what exactly his official title was. His rueful face under a bowler hat appeared with many of the little groups standing by wagons as they were photographed. His actual role seems to have been general factotum and trouble-shooter.

Asked about her father's relationship with the men he employed Mrs.White commented that he was extremely strict in his dealings with them, requiring total obedience, undivided loyalty and reasonable honesty. Though he did not bother himself overmuch with the way in which they conducted themselves when away from work he would not countenance drunkenness when on duty. She added that he was just as strict with his children but that with a family of eight he could hardly have been expected to be otherwise. The drivers who were with him for the whole or the greater part of the life of the firm such as Boarer, Burden, Manktelow and Springett on the traction engines and Harry Reader on the ploughing engines had all proved themselves in his eyes. They gave him of their best and he, for his part, treated them with respect discussing with them, as friends or equals, how jobs might be done or problems overcome. Since, as we have seen, he did not put them on short time or stand them off altogether when work was scarce and he paid their fines if they were in trouble with the police when on his business their loyalty is, perhaps, understandable.

Reliability on the part of his workmen was very important to him. In order to be economically viable the company had to be run with a minimum of supervisory staff. Jesse Ellis's own time was taken up to a large extent by his never-ending search for sources of work for the engines and rollers and, later, for buyers of steam wagons, the wants of farmers and other customers for the implement and agricultural merchanting sides of the business being attended to by Robert Elfick who was present at the principal markets and waited upon clients on their farms. It could function effectively only when Jesse Ellis could depend upon those he employed, whether gang foremen or individual workmen, to know what he required of them and to do it without having to be continually reminded of what they had to do. He knew, for example, that when he had shown Tom Boarer a boiler that he wanted moved, indicated the plant that he intended Tom to use and visited with him the place where it was to be set, he would not have to be constantly visiting the job whilst it was in hand to see that it was being done properly.

By 1904 the firm employed about 150 men in the works and as drivers and mates on the traction engines, road locomotives and rollers, probably the peak in these departments. How many worked on the road maintenance gangs at the same period is not recorded but they were already in serious and continuing decline by that time and by early 1907 had reached a very low ebb. On March 3, 1907, the employees of the firm gathered at the *Dog and Gun* to make a farewell presentation to William Pearce, a road foreman, leaving in order to join the Kent County Council direct labour force, and, in so doing, perhaps epitomising the reasons for the company's impending demise.

A number of old hands, including Messrs Humphrey, Waghorn, Jupp, Bennett and Mason (jun.), went with Jesse Ellis to his brief resurgence at Allington Forge. At his funeral in 1916 William Humphrey and George Bennett attended to pay their respects for the last time.

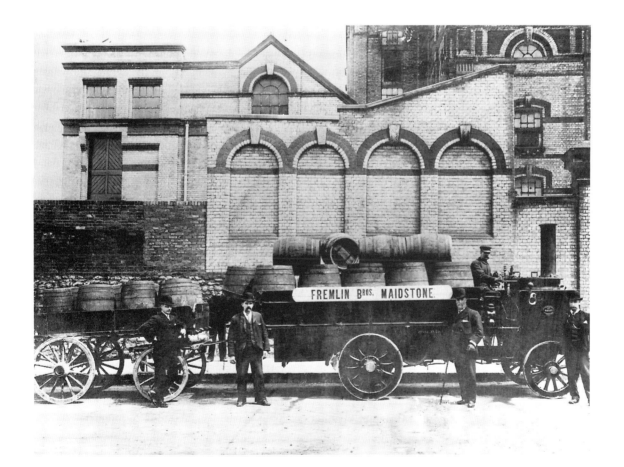

Fig 13: Double framed wagon, with the first type of firetube boiler, posed on Waterside, with Fremlins name on a loose board. They did not buy it and it was quite possibly the wagon that went to Egypt in November, 1902. The figures (l.to r.) are unknown, Tom Town, Jesse Ellis, Offen, and Tom Mason (sen.)

Fig 14:
Aveling & Porter crane engine(No.1810 of 1882), Ellis No.12,at Sittingbourne when owned by W.Ovenden.

Fig 15:
The scene in Mill Street, after the boiler explosion. Clements' builders works on the left.

Fig 16:
The front ring of the burst boiler with the cylinder block still attached.

Chapter 5

THE BOILER EXPLOSION

During the autumn of 1880, in his continual search for business, Jesse Ellis secured a contract that involved hauling manure through Maidstone. Accounts vary as to whether this was of human or lower animal origin but its source is not important in relation to the events that are about to be narrated. It is, however, relevant to note that under the powers given to it under the Highways and Locomotives Act, 1878, Maidstone Borough Council had made regulations that limited the passage of such traffic through its streets to the hours between midnight and 6a.m. Accordingly the haulage in this case had to be done by night.

The engine involved, an 8NHP single cylindered Aveling & Porter two speed road locomotive, No.1302, was relatively new, having been built in 1877. Its boiler must, however, have had a hard time in the intervening three and a half years, as the evidence given at the subsequent inquest was to show.

The journey upon which it was engaged began at the wharf behind Monckton's paper mills on the east bank of the River Medway a little to the north of Maidstone Barracks and should have ended at a farm on the Sutton Road, not far from the cemetery. From the wharf the route ran up the lane to Sandling Road, and into the town, passing the County Gaol and the East Station and turning down St.Faith Street to Waterside along which it proceeded southwards as far as the approach to the New Bridge. The engine was stopped in Waterside to fill the tanks and again near Garrett's foundry to change to low gear for the climb up to the bridge level. It was then taken up the fairly steep slope onto the east approach of the bridge, continuing eastwards along the High Street as far as the entrance of Mill Street, on the south side, into which the driver turned it. A part way along Mill Street a lamp was found to have gone out and the train was stopped to allow it to be relit. As the engine was restarted the boiler exploded.

The gang carrying out the work had been made up of a young driver named Moses ("Moey") Martin, in charge, Frank Underwood as steersman, and Harry Reader, one of the steam ploughing drivers, acting as flagman. Martin was in his twenty-fifth year. He had begun his working life at the age of thirteen as a cook boy with a steam ploughing gang in Essex. By the time he was fifteen he had learned to drive an engine and by the age of sixteen was in sole charge of one. Previously to working for Jesse Ellis he had spent about twelve months with Thomas Wood at Crockenhill, near Swanley. In answer to a question at the later inquest, Jesse Ellis replied that he had taken on Martin originally as a driver on a week's trial without having had a character from his previous employer but that later he had sent a message to Thomas Wood who confirmed in reply that Martin was a good driver though "somewhat abusive on the road". From this one infers that he was voluble at swearing.

Moses Martin had started work at about 6a.m. on December 2. He had been driving one of a pair of engines carting stone at Stockbury, on the Maidstone to Sittingbourne road, the driver of the other being Tom Boarer. The two engines had left Stockbury between two and three in the afternoon, bound for Maidstone but after about an hour and a half on the road a leak in the firebox of Martin's engine had become so bad that he could keep up neither the working pressure nor the water level. As a result he had had to abandon the engine in a field and return as a passenger on Tom Boarer's engine. He finished work that afternoon about half past six. During the evening he went to the office to report to Jesse Ellis. Because his own engine was stranded in the field on the way from Stockbury clearly another engine had to be found to do the night's work. Boarer's engine, available in the yard, still with a fire in it, was the obvious - perhaps the only - candidate. In ordinary circumstances,under Jesse Ellis's policy of 'one man, one engine', Tom Boarer would have gone with it but he had just injured his arm and could not go. Against normal practice, therefore, Martin was sent out on the job but with Boarer's engine instead of his own. On his way from seeing his employer he called at the *Dragoon* beerhouse in Sandling Road with Jim Springett for a couple of pints of beer and had to endure a certain amount of chaffing from his mate about the night's work he was about to begin, to which Martin retorted that the next night he would get Springett a similar job. Moey was known to be an extravagant talker and from the evidence given at the inquest he seems to have displayed a certain amount of bravado about his methods of driving. As is often the case, words spoken without much thought in an exchange of repartee can sound damning when repeated literally by witnesses in a court of law and this is what was about to happen to Moey. Braggartry in the *Dragoon* was to lead him into trouble as, one may infer, it had done on earlier occasions.

Lance-corporal John Leadbetter of the Army Hospital Corps, stationed in Maidstone Barracks, who had overheard the banter between Springett and Martin in the *Dragoon,* later testified at the inquest that he had heard Martin tell Springett that he had been speaking to Mr.Ellis about the engine and that he had to go with it the next day (i.e. beginning at midnight) and that he (Martin) had said "I will have 200lbs of steam into the -------" either by a certain time in the morning or by a certain place. Leadbetter could not remember which.

After having already worked a twelve hour day Martin thus embarked on a strenuous night's work without real rest. Though perhaps to be deprecated, this was not quite the recipe for disaster subsequently suggested before the coroner. In the comfort of a modern motor lorry cab it would probably have introduced a danger of dropping off to sleep but the possibilities of dozing on the manstand of a steel-wheeled unsprung traction engine are, to say the least, not great.

The explosion happened between the workshop of Clements, the builder, on the east side of Mill Street and the graveyard of All Saints Church on the west side. It was a dark night and the blast blew out all the gas street lamps. Constable Little of the Borough Police was on duty in the High Street. He came running, closely followed by Inspector Dalton who had been standing on the bridge. They tripped over fragments of the engine scattered across the road. Soon they were joined by householders, one of whom, Mr.Wakeford, crossed the road with the intention of relighting the gas lamp over the urinal by the burial ground. In the darkness he stumbled over the body of Frank Underwood, the steersman, half naked in a pool of blood with his skull stove in. Another householder, named Relf, fetched some coloured carnival flares from his house and by their bizarre light the horror-struck rescuers saw the extent of the damage.

Underwood was seen to have been blown high into the air, passing through three trees in which his coat and other clothing could be seen. He had struck the ground head first and had died instantly. Harry Reader, walking ahead, had been hit by a piece of iron and had a broken arm. Moses Martin had scalds. It took some minutes to find them but they then managed the walk to the West Kent Hospital, which may well have taken them twenty minutes in their shocked state. Underwood's body was carried into the nearby *Globe* public house.

The police notified Mr.J.B.Stephens, the Borough Coroner, of what had happened. Stephens was a solicitor and a partner in the Maidstone firm of Stephens & Urmston. He ordered them to see that nothing was touched until seen and recorded. Notwithstanding this instruction Thomas Aveling, having heard of the accident, managed to visit the site with one of his foremen and remove the spring balances and their appurtenances. When Stephens opened the inquest later in the day so that Underwood's body could be formally identified - this was done by George Batey, the Ellis & Co. foreman, as Jesse himself was still on his way back from Oxford - he was extremely scathing in his comments on Aveling's action.

At the time of the explosion the engine had two traction wagons behind it. Though evidence as to the load this might have constituted was bandied about at the inquest no one had had the sense to put them onto a weighbridge to determine their actual weight. The opinions as to what the likely weight of the loads was were given by witnesses whose individual interests were likely to be served by understating it.

George Batey stated that the pressure gauge when located had showed a pressure of 250lbs, that the spring balances were light and that they had been screwed down to a pressure of 120lbs, though, he added, they were not screwed completely down and he could have screwed them down another 10lbs. At a later hearing he had to retract that statement. After his evidence and evidence from Tom Boarer the inquest was adjourned to Wednesday, December 15th when no evidence was taken and it was again adjourned until December 22.

A commendable amount of expert evidence had been assembled in the meantime for presentation to the coroner and his assessor. Furthermore, Aveling & Porter had provided a drawing of the boiler; a series of photographs of the scene of the accident had been commissioned from Clarke the Maidstone photographer; and a model of the boiler had been made illustrating in red lines the paths of the fractures. Samples of plate taken from the boiler and corresponding samples of new plates of the same quality as those used in its making had been submitted for testing to Professor Alex B.W.Kennedy at the laboratory of University College, London, presumably also at the expense of Aveling & Porter. In addition Aveling & Porter had provided a model to demonstrate the way in which the spring balance safety valves had been mounted on the exploded boiler. They also put in an example of a spring loaded safety valve to illustrate a point Thomas Aveling was to make in his evidence. The remains of the engine were inspected on December 15th by Mr.William H.Maw, the eminent consulting engineer who was also Editor of *Engineering.* He later gave reasoned and telling evidence at the adjourned inquest. Jesse Ellis & Co and Aveling & Porter were each represented by solicitors, Messrs. Stenning (of Maidstone) and Prall (of Rochester) respectively but Moses Martin who, as the driver, was the man whose livelihood and liberty were at stake had no lawyer to guide him or protect his interests.

The description of the engine and boiler, taken from the report in *Engineering* was as follows:-

The traction engine of which the boiler exploded was one constructed by Messrs. Aveling & Porter, between three and four years ago, and was rated by the makers as an 8-horse. It had a single 9in. cylinder, with 12in. stroke, the driving wheels, which were 5ft.6in. in diameter, being geared to the crankshaft in the ratio of 1 to 16 for the fast speed, and 1 to 25 for the slow speed. In the slow speed gear the engine could thus exert (less, of course, the reduction due to friction of the gear) a pull of 368lb. at the circumference of the driving wheels for each pound of effective pressure per square inch in the cylinder. Thus with a mean effective pressure of 70lb. per square inch on the piston, the pull exerted at the circumference of the driving wheels would amount to 25,760lb., or about 11½ tons, less the internal frictional resistances of the engine. We mention this because from circumstances to which we shall allude hereafter, it appears to us to have a decided bearing on certain aspects of the case.

The boiler was of the usual locomotive type. The barrel was 2ft.10in. in diameter outside, and was composed of plates nominally ⅜in. thick, but in reality slightly thicker. The smokebox tube plate was ⅝in. thick, the back and front plates of the firebox casing were ⅝in thick, while the side plates of the firebox casing (which also formed the horn-plates carrying the bearings of the various shafts) were ½in. thick. The barrel was made up in two rings united by a butt joint and outside welt strip ⅜in. thick, each ring being made up of two plates. In the case of the ring next the firebox the upper plate extended rearwards and formed the crown of the firebox casing. the flanged plates - namely, the smokebox tube plate and the front and back plates of the firebox casing - were of 'Tudhoe best best' iron, while the under plate of the ring of the barrel next firebox was of 'Monkbridge best', and the rest of the shell of 'Tudhoe crown' iron. The transverse joints were single rivetted with rivets eleven sixteenths in. diameter placed at 1⅜in. pitch, while the longitudinal joints were double rivetted with rivets of the same size placed at 2¼in. pitch. The inside firebox was of Lowmoor iron throughout, the plates being ⅜in. thick, with the exception of the tube plate, which was ⅝in. The firebox stays were of a special quality of Tudhoe scrap made expressly for such purposes. The firebox stays were ¾in., and the longitudinal stays 1in. in diameter; the upper longitudinal stays were secured at the rear ends to stiff T-irons by ⅞in. pins passing through forked eyes. The boiler contained 33 tubes 2½in. in diameter outside, the heating surface of these tubes being 115.6 square feet. The grate area was 5.9 square feet. The boiler was altogether well-proportioned and it is stated to have had excellent steaming power. The cylinder was mounted on the boiler and fixed by eight bolts 1in. in diameter passing through the base, these bolts being a tight fit through the boiler shell, and having large square heads inside. Also, two nipples each 3⅛in. in diameter were screwed through the barrel plate and cylinder base, these nipples connecting the steam space of the boiler with the cylinder jacket, this jacket also forming the steam dome, and the steam being drawn from it for the use of the engine. On the top of the cylinder jacket were provided two safety valves, each 2¼in. in diameter, these valves being loaded by ordinary levers and spring balances, and the latter being provided with ferrules. According to Messrs. Aveling & Porter's book of rules issued for the use of the engine drivers of their traction engines, the proper working pressure for the boiler we are describing was 100lb. per square inch, and as was shown by the evidence, the spring balances on leaving Messrs. Aveling & Porter's works were ferruled so that they could not be screwed down to give a pressure exceeding 110lb. per square inch. The highest pressure to which the spring balances were graduated was 120lb. per square inch.

The same source gives a clear description of the damage sustained to the boiler:-

An examination of the remains of the boiler, which we were able to make on the 15th inst., showed that the plates were in good order, there being no signs of furrowing or corrosion, nor, as far as the shell was concerned, any signs of local weakness. In the case of the firebox, however, the remains showed that there had been a serious crack in the left-hand side plate, and that this crack instead of having been cut out and repaired by a patch, had been merely plugged by copper studs, of which no less than nine had been screwed in. The position of these studs appeared to indicate either that there had originally been two cracks which had eventually joined into one, or that the crack had had a V-form. In the view of the cracked plate, the copper plugs are marked AA, while at BBBB, are shown the positions of the firebox stays, the middle vertical row of these stays being directly on the line of the chief part of the crack. When the explosion occurred the rupture extended completely to the top and bottom of the plate as shown, the plate being at the same time bulged inwards, as indicated. From this latter view it will be seen that the right-hand side plate was also bulged inwards but not to so great an extent.

The remaining plates of the firebox were not ruptured, but they were considerably distorted, the tube plate being bulged *outwards* or towards the water space, it apparently having been drawn into that form by the pull of the tubes before they left their holes, most of the tubes remaining fixed in the smokebox tube plate. The crown plate was dished deeply downwards, but the roof stays had bent without fracture, and none of the bolts securing the crown to these stays had failed. The major part of the back plate of the firebox casing remained attached to the back plate of the firebox by the firehole ring and by the stays; six of these stays, however, apparently having been fractured at some time prior to the explosion. The back plate of the firebox was bulged inward about ⅜in. between the stays, which remained sound. There was a crack, apparently of old date, at the ring at the right hand lower corner of the firebox, but this crack was not of importance.

A clear idea of the manner in which the shell was ripped up will be gained by an examination of the illustrations better than from any verbal description. It will be seen that the back plate of the firebox casing parted around the root of the flange for nearly its entire circumference, the side plates and crown plates attached to it apparently turning on the line of fracture as on a hinge. The firebox stays for the most part remained in the side plates of the firebox casing, being mostly drawn from the firebox plates. The fractures in the side plates are clearly indicated, as are also those on the front plate of the firebox casing. In this latter case it will be noticed that there is a rip right round the root of the flange which meets the barrel of the boiler, this rip also extending down the root of the vertical flange on the right-hand side and through the line of rivet holes of the bottom ring. In the barrel there is a longitudinal rip along the line of rivets on each side of the ring next the firebox, and a circumferential rip through one line of rivets of the welt ring. In front of this the rip took a spiral course through the front ring of plates, crossing one of the longitudinal seams as shown, and ultimately terminating in the line of rivets by which the smokebox tube plate was fixed. The general appearance of this front ring of plates after the explosion is shown by the perspective view.

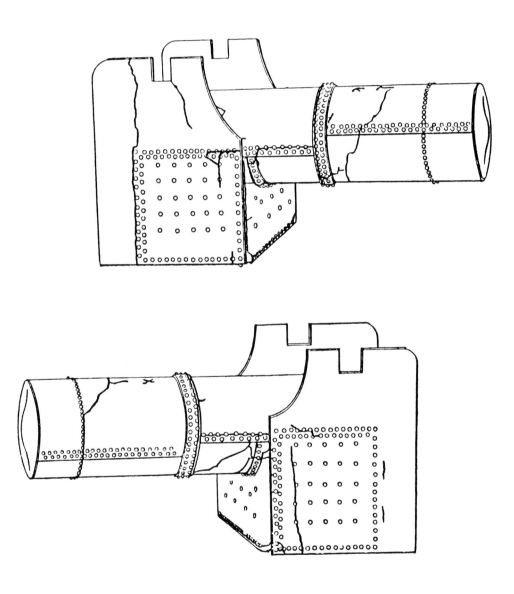

Figs 17 and 18: Drawings showing the lines of failure of the boiler plates.

Chapter 6

On December 22 the twice adjourned inquest on the body of Frank Underwood began. It had been arranged that Mr.T.J.Richards of the Marine Department of the Board of Trade should sit with Mr.Stephens as an assessor. Stephens dealt only with legal procedures and questions of law confining himself otherwise to reading the evidence of Batey and Boarer given on December 3 and to questions of an introductory nature to each new witness. All technical questions were left to Mr.Richards. The Coroner sat with a jury who must have felt somewhat at sea with the technical evidence.

The redoubtable Tom Boarer was then recalled so that he could be further questioned by Mr.Richards. He explained that the reason why Martin and not he was driving the engine on the night of December 2 and 3 was because he had hurt his arm during the preceding day. Whilst he said that he usually worked the boiler at 100lbs pressure he agreed that he sometimes exceeded this when he had to take loads up-hill. At these times, he said, he "had as much pressure as he wanted". Presumably by this he meant that on such occasions he screwed down the valves until the engine had sufficient power to tackle the gradient. He said the maximum he had used was 125lbs and that he had never needed more for any road or load. His foreman had told him, he went on, that the proper pressure was 100lbs and that he was not to exceed this *unless he required it,* but he averred that no maximum limit had been mentioned. He had told both his foreman and Mr.Ellis that he had loads which needed more than 100lbs pressure in order to deal with them and was told in reply not to load too heavily. He had had one such heavy load on the last day (December 2) he had worked the exploded engine, 14 cubic yards of stone, which he found he could manage except on hills, where extra pressure was required.

The assessor then examined him closely concerning the state of the safety valves and the repair that had been done to the firebox:-

When he took charge of the engine, the safety valve ferrules were in the same condition as at the time of the explosion. He never took ferrules off, and he knew that if the ferrules were taken off valves could be screwed down. He never reduced the ferrules, and did not know that anyone had done so; he did not always keep the levers screwed down to ferrules, but generally kept spring balances so that the valve blew off at 100lb. He knew that when the spring balances were screwed down to ferrules the valves could not blow off freely, but he never so screwed them down. He thought he could lift levers about ¼in. when they were screwed down to the ferrules, but the distance might be less; he had never tried it. He had never screwed spring balances nearer to the ferrules than ½in.; the steam would then blow off at 100lb. He acknowledged, however, that he screwed them down further to get 125lb., but maintained that he did not screw them home. Stated that he left space equal to the thickness of a penny; in that position of the spring balances the steam blew off at 125lb. Had compared blowing off pressure as shown by spring balances with indications of the steam gauge and found that the spring balances were weak, and that there was a difference of pressure between them and the gauge of about 15lb.; he had mentioned this to the foreman, who had not done anything to the spring balances. The steam gauge was new and had been on about two months, it had not been examined since. He gave up charge of the engine to Martin on the evening before the accident. The spring balances were then screwed down to within about ¼in. of ferrules; he gave Martin no special instructions about the engine, neither did he mention how the safety valves had been left. He did not know what Martin was going to do; he was told later on that he was going to work at night hauling manure. He had seen cracked firebox plate first about six months ago, the copper studs were then put in; he discovered the crack himself, and all the nine copper studs were put in at the same time, and no repairs were done subsequently. The crack started leaking round one of the studs, he believed about the centre of the crack; nothing was done as the leak sometimes stopped. Copper studs were put in instead of putting on a patch. He thought these plugs strengthened the plate; he could not say if this was the proper way of dealing with the crack, but it stopped the leak, and was often done. On the day prior to the accident there was no more leakage than during the previous month; he knew of another firebox repaired by studs at Messrs. Ellis & Co's works. He thought that the crack in that case was about 4in. long; he had never complained of the manner in which the firebox of the exploded boiler was repaired, he had told Mr.Ellis and the foreman that it leaked. The boiler never leaked anywhere else.

After Mr.Richards had concluded his questioning Mr.Stenning, appearing for Jesse Ellis & Co, asked Tom Boarer if he had had a copy of Aveling & Porter's rules and also a copy of the rules of Jesse Ellis & Co. Mr.Stenning was clearly out to disprove his statement that no maximum pressure had ever been put to him. Did not the rules, he asked, state that a driver would be fined one shilling if he allowed the boiler pressure to exceed 125lb. The witness agreed this was so.

In answer to a further question from Mr.Stenning he said he had previously worked for another engine owner named Bowles by whom cracks were repaired in the same way, i.e. by filling with a chain of copper studs and he knew of other owners who had adopted the same method.

The Coroner asked if he had ever been fined. Boarer said no and that, so far as he knew, no other driver had either, though he had been cautioned against blowing off steam along the road and also against carrying more than 100lb. pressure.

A juryman asked if the boiler had been examined whilst he had been the driver of the engine. Boarer replied that, in the ten months he had been in charge of it, it had been regularly washed out but had had no other examination. After this he was allowed to stand down.

The next witness to be called was Moses Martin, with a patch over one eye and still showing signs of .the other injuries he had received in the accident. Before questions were put the Coroner informed him that he was not bound to answer any that might incriminate him. He was then questioned about his experience as a driver and the handing over of the engine to him the night before. He said Tom Boarer had given him no instructions and that he had never had charge of it before although he had ridden home on it merely as a passenger on December 2. When he took it over the pressure was about 25lb. and he got this up to 75lb. at which pressure, of course, it did not blow off steam. He said he had not altered the spring balances when he took it over, adding that it was then dark. In fact he did not look at the safety valve or spring balances when he took charge or at any other time before the explosion. He did not touch the nuts on the balances and these were in the same condition at the time of the explosion as when he took the engine over. It would not be altogether surprising if he had been put pretty much out of temper by the events of December 2 - the breakdown of his regular engine and his having to do the manure carting with an unfamiliar engine which, from what Boarer himself had said earlier, that worthy would have been driving himself had he not damaged his arm.

He was then asked about the period just before the explosion. He explained that the only reason he had stopped the engine in Mill Street was to relight the lamp that had gone out. The engine had stopped more or less on dead centre and he had had to reverse it to get started. One can picture what might have taken place; a tired and impatient young man, not in a good temper at the outset, irritated at the lamp having gone out and cross with himself for having stopped the engine straight-arm so that he could not restart without reversing it. That start is likely to have been pretty rough, the last straw to an already overstressed and poorly repaired boiler. He was closely questioned about that journey from Monckton's Mill:

The safety vales did not blow off when he stopped. The steam jet was not in use. He had seen the safety valves blow off strongly coming up from Mr.Monckton's mill. Just before the explosion the pressure was 120lb., and it might have been 125lb. when steam blew off as above stated; the engine was "blowing off terrific". He could see the steam gauge perfectly well, as he had a hand lamp, and he looked at the gauge every few minutes, same as if it had been daylight. Steam also blew off at Wharf Lane. He did not think it possible for any one to alter the valves without his seeing it. Underwood (the deceased) was the steersman and Reader was the man in advance. Had an excellent clear fire at the time of the explosion as he had Stone Street before him, and this was a hill, though not a steep one. Last took in water three-quarters of an hour before explosion. He had no opinion as to the cause of the explosion except that the safety valves might have got set, which they frequently did. He thought it possible that they might have set fast between leaving Mr.Monckton's mill and the explosion. He had a load of two wagons with about five tons of manure in each, and he had no difficulty in taking this load up any of the hills. He did not remember engine making any particular noise on the night of the explosion. If the steam got too high he could blow it back into the tender; he never did this on the night of the explosion. He was in the act of starting the engine when the explosion occurred, and the engine made about one revolution when the boiler burst. He did not remember anything more. The water was up to the top of the gauge glass at the time. He last stopped prior to the explosion opposite Mr.Garrett's foundry to change into slow speed gear.

Mr.Stenning then questioned him about events on the afternoon of December 2, and the breakdown of his own engine. He asked him at what pressure Boarer's engine was then working. Martin replied, seemingly with asperity, that he did not know. He was next questioned about priming, both specifically on the exploded engine and also in general. He replied thus:

On the night of the explosion the engine primed after taking water at the town wharf, when going up the hill near the bridge, where the road had been newly laid with stones. Having water too high caused the mud to boil up and get into the cylinder and safety valves. By priming he meant the presence of water in the cylinder. He heard this priming, but it did not pull engine up. He did not know about the spring balances being light, but knew of the crack in the firebox, as he heard it hiss. He knew the method of mending cracks in fireboxes by copper studs; he had seen this plan followed in nearly every county in England. It was the ordinary way of mending such a crack. He did not consider that there was any danger from the crack. By valves being "set" he meant valves being fixed by dirt. He had often known this to happen in valves similar to those on the boiler which exploded.

Mr.Richards questioned him about the repair that had been carried out to his regular engine by filling a crack with copper studding, the failure of which had caused its breakdown on the way home from Stockbury. Why, he asked Martin, had he stopped the engine before it had reached the end of its journey? Martin's answer was quite short.- because he would not run risks; he could not keep up the water level and the leak damped the fire so that he could not keep up steam. He again said that during the ride home he had not looked at either the pressure gauge or the safety valves of Boarer's engine.

It was now the turn of Mr.Prall, appearing for Aveling & Porter. After a few opening questions of dubious relevance to the inquiry concerning how Martin had first worked with engines he asked him what was the highest pressure at which he had worked an engine. The reply was 125lb. Had he known an engine to be worked at higher pressure? Yes, Martin snapped, he had seen such a thing happen twice. On one occasion it was on a Fowler ploughing engine at Coggeshall, Essex. It had exploded! Yes, he had seen pressure gauges *showing* more than 125lb. but only because they were light. He had never shortened a ferrule on a spring balance safety valve or known of one being shortened nor had he, as far as he was aware, driven an engine without a ferrule or with one that had been shortened. He could not say whether the engine that exploded had a ferrule or not.

In reply to a juror he said that he had started from Monckton's mill with a good supply of water. At the time of the explosion he was on the tender and the firehole door was open. The ashpan damper had been closed all the way up the High Street. He agreed, answering Mr.Stenning, that he had a copy of Aveling & Porter's rules and also of those of the firm, which he was given when he began working for them. At this juncture Martin was allowed to stand down.

After Martin the next witness was George Batey, the foreman. After having been taken through the salient points of his career he was subjected to a searching series of questions on the company's system of inspection and repair, his views on the method of repairing cracks in the firebox plates by the use of copper studs and his opinions on how the laws regulating the use of traction engines affected operational safety. This is the summary of his evidence, from the report in *Engineering:*

He examined Messrs. Ellis & Co's engines and boilers as far as possible both internally and externally. He usually examined them at intervals of seven to eight months, when opportunity offered. He had no fixed period of examination, and no other engineer examined them. He did not consider himself responsible for the condition of the boilers, but only for what he did himself, and what was done to them under his supervision. He could not say who was responsible for the engines. He generally consulted Mr.Ellis as to repairs. He had given no definite orders to Boarer regarding steam pressure; he had generally warned the drivers not to get pressure too high. He might have said that it was unnecessary to get more than 125lb. pressure when they got into bad places. They could not always do with one set pressure; about 125lb. was the highest pressure he had known to be used, and he did not think that pressure would hurt the boiler which had exploded. He considered that 125lb. might be employed occasionally, but he would not advise its continually being used. Could not say that drivers had ever exceeded 125lb., but could not, on the other hand, say they had not. He could not say that the ferrules of the spring balances on the engine which exploded had been reduced, he had never reduced any ferrules. The latter were soldered on to the spring balances to prevent their removal. He did not know of any way in which the safety valves would be overloaded when steam was up, except by placing weights on the levers. Did not know that, with the ferrules as they were in the case of the exploded boilers, levers could be loaded to more than 125lb. He did not think it would be possible to set the valves fast with the ferrules in place. Could not say when he last gave Boarer any special instructions respecting the engine which exploded. Did not see Boarer on the night of December 2 but gave Martin directions to take the engine. Boarer had told him that it had been necessary to have 125lb. pressure, in consequence of the roads being in a heavy state. Spoke to Martin on the night before the explosion,and he (Martin) said that "if they can't do the work with 120lb. steam, they must have more". To the best of his recollection, Martin said, that if 120lb. will not do "they" must have 180lb. He (Batey) then remarked that if he had the power he would discharge any engine driver that got to 180lb. Nothing more was said. He did not think it necessary to examine valves of the engine Martin was going to take out, to see if the ferrules were alright. He did not know why Martin made the remark about steam pressure, but the roads were in a very heavy state. Estimated the load which Martin was drawing at the time of the explosion at about 11 or 12 tons. This would be about the ordinary load. he could not say what inducement there could be for a driver to exceed 125lb.; the drivers were told not to draw unduly heavy loads; they sometimes got into a hole, but they could get out again without exceeding a pressure of 125lb. He did not in any way examine the boiler on the day prior to the explosion. He last examined the engine at harvest time, when the engine was going out thrashing. He did not then specially examine the ferrules, but believed they were alright. He had not satisfied himself whether the safety valves were or were not free to act at the time of the explosion. He believed the latter was caused by excessive pressure. Did not think the boiler would have exploded at 125lb., the pressure must have been something more. He could not form any opinion about the excessive pressure and how it was attained. He considered that the safety valves could not have been free to act; he could not state the cause. Did not know whether they were set fast by dirt, or had been screwed down. The sketches exhibited fairly showed the condition of the firebox of exploded boiler; the firebox was repaired by one of his men under his orders; any one could put in copper studs. The studs had been put in at different times, as the crack had extended. Could not give the dates when studs were put in; he had simply sent a man to do what was necessary, he did not see the work done himself. If they had found that the crack required so many studs at once, most likely a patch would have been put on. Putting in plugs was a common practice. The crack would be apt to permit a stay in it to draw, and the plugs would not prevent this. He did not consider the insertion of copper studs the safest way of repairing a crack, neither did he think, however, that this mode of repairing was the cause of the boiler having given way. When at Messrs Aveling & Porter's works, he would not have been allowed to repair a boiler in that way, and if the engine had been at the works, he would have preferred putting a patch on. Sometimes an engine came in late at night, and had to go out in the morning. He did not remember that he had ever expressed a wish to repair this firebox by patching. Messrs J.Ellis & Co had one other firebox with copper studs in it, the crack in that case was, he believed, about 4 or 5in. long. He did not think this a safe way of repairing a firebox worked at 125lb. He had told Mr.Ellis that in such cases he would prefer patching, and in some cases when there was time, this was done. In other cases studs had been put in. They were not allowed to haul manure through the town of Maidstone during the day. As a rule their men were not sent out at night except when hauling manure, but sometimes they worked on into the night for special jobs. He considered that it was a great inconvenience to work an engine at night, it was dangerous, and might lead to serious accident. There was a bye-law to the effect that engines should not blow off steam in traversing the streets. This he considered a bad law, as it led to the men getting up to tap the valves to keep the steam from blowing off. If the steam was kept in, the pressure rose fast, and was likely to explode the boiler.If the men let the steam blow off they were fined, and if they let the steam down and made smoke getting it up again, they were liable to prosecution. Only last week one of their men had been threatened with a fine for allowing the steam to blow off through the valves. The man had asked him (Batey) what to do, and he replied that he did not know exactly. They could direct the steam into the tender through the waste steam cock, but he did not think this gave sufficient relief. Moreover, they had sometimes no water in the tender to condense the steam.

At this point in his evidence the court adjourned for a short interval. When it resumed he had modified somewhat his opinion of the merits and demerits of copper studding as a method of repair. Cross-examined by Mr.Stenning on behalf of the firm he became evasive and rather contradictory in his answers:

Since he had been connected with engineering it had been the custom to mend cracks in the fireboxes with copper studs; he had never known any accident to result from this. He had been in the employment of eminent engineers; he had been assistant-foreman to Messrs. Easton & Anderson for eight months; and also (as had been stated) he had been with Messrs.Aveling & Porter, and the remainder of the time with traction engine proprietors; two and a half years with Messrs. Chittenden & Knight, who had about 35 to 40 engines, and for seven years with Mr.Thomas Wood, who possessed 18 or 20 engines. All the engine owners with whom he had worked, except Mr.Aveling, made it a practice to mend cracks in the fireboxes with copper studs, provided that the cracks were not too long. He did not have any boilers to repair when at Messrs.Easton & Anderson's, and could not speak as to their practice. He did not think it dangerous to mend cracks in the manner adopted in the exploded boiler, provided that too many studs were not put in; and he did not think the repair of the exploded firebox had been dangerous. The studs would not weaken the firebox; if there was a crack the studs would stop the water from coming out but would not strengthen the plate. He considered the crack in the exploded boiler was not conducive to ,neither had it anything to do with, the explosion. The effect of the crack was to allow water to put the fire out. The cracked plate would probably go first, and put out the fire. He considered this not a safe way of repairing cracks of this description: if so repaired it might leak again in a week or so. What he meant by improper repair was inserting studs loosely. Was of the opinion that the utmost harm that could happen to the engine by reason of such crack, or from being improperly mended with copper studs, would be to allow steam and water to escape into the firebox and put the fire out. This was exactly what he meant. There was nothing more dangerous in inserting plugs than by mending by patching; the word "safe" he used as meaning the power of holding the cracked plate together.

After this hard handling by Mr.Stenning he must have, figuratively at least, wiped his brow. Mr.Prall, for Aveling & Porter, put the question of whether or not he considered it dangerous to work engines by night. Batey agreed it was more dangerous in the dark. Lamps had the habit of going out and drivers could not see well. It was harder to start an engine in the dark (because, one assumes, it was more difficult to see the position of the crank) and to manage the loads. Questioned about 125lb. as a maximum pressure, he considered it not dangerous as the boiler was tested when new to 200lb. Asked about his earlier reference to remarks about pressures alleged to have been made by Martin he said that it would be easy to reduce the loads on bad roads and thus avoid any necessity for the excessive pressure alluded to by Martin. Drivers were supposed to limit the load to that which a pressure of 125lb. would enable the engine to draw. When questioned about the loads that Martin was required to draw on the fatal night he was able to say only that they were not excessive even for roads in bad condition. Had he weighed the loads? No, he agreed, he spoke only from having looked at them.

One of the jurymen asked him if he inspected all repairs at the time they were executed. Batey said he did not, emphasising his answer by remarking that he did not inspect the insertion of every copper stud. No juryman, however, appeared to notice or comment upon the discrepancy between what Boarer had said about the insertion of the copper studs and what Batey had just testified. The former had said that they had all been put in at once when he first reported the crack but Batey's evidence was that they had gone in over a period of time as the crack had lengthened.

After him in the witness box came Corporal Leadbetter who repeated on oath the remarks he said he had overheard in the *Dragoon* on the evening of December 2. He was followed in turn by Jim Springett who confirmed he had been in the *Dragoon* with Martin and had chaffed him about night-work but denied that any discussion occurred on boiler pressures. George Tolhurst, another Jesse Ellis & Co employee present in the *Dragoon* at the same time as Martin and Springett, confirmed what Springett had said and could not remember anything being said about boiler pressures.

The flagman, Harry Reader, was called next and corroborated what Martin had testified earlier about the safety valves having been in working order during the early part of the journey. His own opinion was that the explosion was the result of the safety valves sticking. A juryman asked him if he, too, had been in the *Dragoon*. He said not and in response to a further question observed that Martin was perfectly sober.

William Hunt, son of the landlady of the *Dragoon*, and a police constable who had been on duty in the High Street both gave evidence but said little of substance. They were the last of the lesser players. It remained to examine Jesse Ellis himself and Thomas Aveling.

Jesse Ellis came first. Not being used to interviews in which he was not in the dominant position he seems to have attempted to outface the Board of Trade assessor and to stonewall his questions. As the examination proceeded it became apparent that he was mistaken in this endeavour. T.J.Richards was far more practised in such examinations than was Jesse Ellis and the latter soon found himself embarrassed. Led by the opening questions he explained that he was a traction engine proprietor and had bought the engine in question new from Aveling & Porter. With it he had received a book in which it was stated that the working pressure was 100lb. The book did not say this pressure was not to be exceeded. To his discomfiture the book was produced and he had to admit that it stated the *maximum* pressure to be 100lb. Asked what his instructions were to his drivers he replied that they were told not to exceed 100lb. except when in difficulty. What, asked his tormentor, was the definition of a difficulty? After some attempts at evasion he had to admit that it meant any impediment to progress that could not be surmounted on 100lb. pressure. The men were told that on no account were they to go above 125lb. If they had an extra heavy load they could always take up one truck at a time.
"When you received the engine from Aveling & Porter were the ferrules adjusted to 100lb.?"
"I cannot say."
"Have they since been reduced?"
"Not to my knowledge."
On further probing he agreed he could not say what had been done. He had told

Batey to arrange that the ferrules were adjusted to 100lb. He had no knowledge of them being since reduced.

"Was the boiler inspected by an independent engineer?"

"Not to my knowledge."

At this point his answers had begun to approach the absurd, as he must have realised. Richards allowed him a respite by asking a simple question about the provenance of the pressure gauge. He then dropped in an apparently innocuous question:

"Have you ever known a safety valve to be overloaded?"

"Never."

The lion was now well and truly in the trap. The cylinder block of the exploded engine had been brought into court and the spring balances had been put on again connected to new levers made to correspond exactly with the levers which had been in use at the time of the explosion. Jesse Ellis was then asked to examine this exhibit and to say whether or not the length of ferrule on the spring balances was such as to permit the valve being absolutely locked. After some bridling and hesitation he had to admit it was so.

He was then taken through Batey's evidence on the use of copper studs for the repair of cracks. Had Batey told him, as he said he had, that this method should not be used? No, he had not. When the cracks were too long it was his habit to put on a patch but he did not think it necessary to do so in this case. He did not consider the crack to be serious. He had a larger crack in another firebox - some 5 or 6 inches - and that he considered a serious crack. When the crack went from stay to stay they put on a patch and if they had had the engine which exploded at home they would have put on a patch. In answer to a further question he said he was not aware that he had an engine with an 8 or 9 inch crack. He was not aware of any defect in the burst boiler other than the crack which had been repaired with studs. To what then, he was asked, did he attribute the explosion? He answered that he thought it must have been caused by the valves sticking fast.

Answering a question from his own solicitor, Mr.Stenning, he said he had driven the engine home from Rochester when it was new and that the safety valves worked then though he did not recall at what pressure. He reiterated that in his opinion the crack was not a contributory cause of the explosion. Had it failed it would have put the fire out. Mr. Prall asked him why Batey had soldered the ferrules to the spring balances and he replied , diplomatically, that it was because he had seen it done elsewhere.

The hapless George Batey was recalled. First he was asked about the hours worked by the company's drivers generally and then those worked by Martin on December 2 and 3. More importantly he was next asked to examine the exhibit of the cylinder block with the safety valves reinstated which had left his employer in confusion, after which he had had to agree that they could be locked. This contradicted what he had said in evidence at an earlier point in the hearing and damaged his shaken credibility still further.

It was now the turn of Thomas Aveling. Prompted by skilfully planted questions from his own solicitor, Mr.Prall, he gave a faintly bombastic series of answers, summarized by *Engineering* in this way:

He was a member of the Institution of Civil Engineers, and partner in the firm of Messrs.Aveling & Porter. He was the inventor of agricultural locomotives, one of which he exhibited first at Canterbury in 1860. He had had to grapple with the difficulty of meeting the requirements of the law as to the working of these engines, and he had been consulted in each case when Acts of Parliament controlling the use of such engines had been framed to protect the public. He was of the opinion that if the directions issued with his engines were complied with, there would be no difficulty in fulfilling the requirements of the Act of Parliament. In no town in which he had had experience, had the regulations been more liberal than in Maidstone. His firm had made and sold between 1 600 and 1 700 engines, which were now in use in all parts of the world. It was his practice, as far as possible, to call the attention of purchasers to any breach of the regulations. Every safety valve leaving his works was arranged for a working of 100lb. per square inch; but to prevent the men from being inconvenienced by a few pounds increase of pressure, the spring balances were all ferruled at 110lb.

There was no exception to this rule, and the engines were all passed by three foremen. He estimated the bursting pressure of the boiler which had exploded at 500 to 600lb.; but it would fail with smaller pressure if applied continuously for a long period. He had tested one of these boilers to 300lb. by hydraulic pressure; it was perfectly impossible to lock the safety valves if the ferrules were left in a proper state. After the explosion he found the safety valves of the boiler which had burst, his foreman, Metcalf, Mr.Batey and Mr.Drake [one of the jury] of Maidstone, being present at the time. The ferrules were now in the same condition as when found, and he called attention to their condition at the time. He knew at once when he saw the ferrules that they had been cut down, and were certainly not in the condition in which they left his works. The spring balances when found were taken up by his foreman of engine drivers to Messrs.Drake & Muirhead's to be locked in their safe. Mr.Batey could not then say whether the ferrules were shortened. He was sorry to state that the practice of removing ferrules was a very general one with engine drivers, and he had known a previous explosion of one of his engines from this cause. In that case the ferrules had been taken away altogether. The removal of ferrules was so much the practice that he sent a circular to every customer calling attention to that explosion. He did not now use the same arrangement of safety valves as that on the exploded boiler. He had tried lock-up valves, but gave them up because they found the lock tampered with and the valves overloaded. He had now adopted a new arrangement of direct spring loaded valve, an example of which he exhibited and explained. On the 15th instant, after examining the remains of the exploded boiler, he came across an engine passing the place, both valves of which were locked. This engine belonged to Mr. Bailey, of Cranbrook, and he applied for a summons against him, but the Town Clerk declined to grant it. He had reported the locking of the valves to the owner, and the valves were now altered. He considered that the men overloaded valves from a desire to do all the work possible; they were not aware of the risks they ran. The whole root of the evil was that no attention was paid to the state of the roads in adjusting the loads. Using a high pressure of steam certainly saved trouble in difficult places. It was not correct to state that an engine could not be kept from blowing off; if the smokebox door and firedoor were open, and the damper closed, the waste pipe to the tender would relieve the boiler fully. The waste pipe was ¾in. in diameter. He would, however, like to see the law respecting the blowing off of steam on public roads altered, as it might cause danger with engines in the hands of ignorant men. He had seen a man on an engine who could not read a steam gauge, and when asked to mark 135lb. pointed to 60lb. This had led him (Mr.Aveling) to put a red mark on all his gauges at the working pressure. He knew that ignorant men were frequently placed in charge of these engines, and that public safety was in danger in consequence. He considered that drivers should have certificates, and should not be allowed to pass through populous places without this licence, which would be given to the men who proved their efficiency on examination by competent authorities. The licence should be always carried, and suspended on proof of misconduct. Engines should never be allowed to work at night except under exceptional circumstances, as the difficulties are increased, and they are more dangerous to horses. Men working these engines often have to travel over unknown districts without trustworthy information as to inclines, sources of water supply, &c, and hence the necessity of a superior class of drivers. The method of repair adopted for the firebox of the exploded boiler was a bad one. He did not think that the owner would have adopted it had the engine been at home. It tended to weaken instead of strengthen the plate. The remains of the exploded firebox showed that it had failed in the direct line of the crack; if another plate had failed his remarks perhaps would not have applied, but after seeing the firebox of the exploded boiler the point did not require to be argued. There was, he thought, only one case when studding was to any extent justifiable, namely, when the engine was a long way from home, and it was necessary to work it back. It should then be taken back at low pressure, and the crack patched as soon as the engine arrived at the works. The hold of the stay in the plate was much weakened by the crack, and there was the danger of the stay being drawn through. Plugs would not tighten the the hold of the stays on a plate; there could be no two opinions on that point. There was no proof that either Mr. Ellis or his foreman knew of the extent of this crack, or they would probably have had it patched. Serious and fatal explosions had been caused through the breakage or the drawing through of firebox stays. He considered the explosion had been caused by the valves being locked, and there being consequently excessive pressure. Boilers like that of the exploded engine generate steam very rapidly, especially at high pressures, and when the engines are running at low speeds. He was sure that the top of firebox had been forced down gradually by high pressure prior to the explosion; he judged this from the state of the firebox crown and some broken stay bolts. He was not certain that the explosion occurred in consequence of the condition of the firebox, but thought that if the firebox plate had given way under ordinary pressure the shell generally would not have been as fractured as it was. He regarded the crack in the firebox as dangerous, and knew of no good firm of engineers who would have allowed such a system of repair as that which had been adopted. A load of ten to eleven tons of manure was a heavy load at this time of the year, as the wagons would weigh about six tons, making a total of seventeen to eighteen tons. He did not consider that the load could be drawn at a pressure of 100lb. per square inch in the present state of the road. Soft roads constituted the difficulty, and the roads were now in that bad condition.

That Bailey's name was permitted to have been dragged in suggests weakness on the part of the Coroner. A judge would not have allowed Aveling to take such liberties with the Court. Aside from this, however, Aveling had stated that Jesse Ellis did not know how excess steam in a boiler could be coped with, that the law was wrong in relation to prohibiting the blowing off of steam on the road, that engine men were ignorant, that the repair to the firebox was a bad one. Perhaps his crowning impertinence to the court was his statement that there was no proof that either Jesse Ellis or his foreman knew of the extent of the crack.

Mr. Stenning began a series of questions designed to undo as much as possible of the damage done to his client by Aveling's evidence. Could, he asked, the public see the pressure gauge? They could do so, replied Mr.Aveling, because it was placed high for that very purpose. Should engines be registered? Certainly not. They were all right. It was drivers who required to be registered. Asked if a pressure of 125lb. was dangerous he gave the curious answer that there need be no fear of its effect on the boiler if the balances were properly adjusted but that it would be a dangerous pressure with the spring balances in their present state. Since Mr.Stenning's question had referred to a specific pressure it is hard to see why the presence or absence of effective safety valves could have had any influence on the effect of that pressure. He then reiterated that the boiler would not have exploded had the valves not been locked and that 100lb. pressure should not have been exceeded. "Now", said Mr.Stenning,"you have referred to ignorant men being placed in charge of engines. Have you seen ignorant men driving Messrs.Ellis & Co's engines?" Aveling had to admit that he had not. Asked, however, if he had not seen other fireboxes repaired with copper studs to the same extent as that which was exploded he was on firmer ground and gave a very emphatic negative.

There followed lengthy evidence by Mr.William H.Maw, the consulting engineer who had inspected the remains of the shattered boiler on December 15. He began by giving an account of how he had found it. Led by Mr.Richards, the assessor, he proceeded to describe the effect of excessive pressure upon the boiler and his view of why it had exploded. Since he was the Editor of *Engineering* we may assume that the following summary from that journal was an accurate report:

He had examined the safety valves and spring balances found, and also the remains of the levers, and had satisfied himself that the ferrules were of such length that the valves could be completely locked. The arrangement of valves was one which offered facilities for *wilful* overloading. The direct spring valves now fitted by Messrs.Aveling & Porter were much safer. If tested by a steadily increasing hydraulic pressure, he should expect a new boiler of the same construction as that which exploded to fail as follows: At a pressure of about 250lb. the firebox crown would probably commence to take a permanent set, and its deflection would go on increasing with the increase of pressure, until it assumed a form in which its resistance was equal to that of the sides of the firebox. At a pressure of between 500 and 560lb. the sides of the firebox would probably show signs of failure and give trouble by leakage around the stay-heads; while if the pumping power available was sufficient to overpower this leakage and continue the increase of pressure, he should expect the boiler shell to fail at about 640lb. per square inch. It was, however. possible that some of the firebox stays might draw from the plate before this. A much smaller pressure than would be required to burst the boiler in the above way would, however, suffice to cause failure if applied continuously for a considerable period of time, and especially so if the pressure was varied. It was to meet this, and also to allow for the effects of wear and tear, that the working pressure was made so much less than the bursting pressure. He considered that 100 to 110lb. was a very safe working pressure for the boiler which exploded when in good repair, but he considered that the latter pressure should not be exceeded in the hands of the men who have charge of these engines. The firebox of the exploded boiler was certainly not in good order, and the manner of repairing it was decidedly defective. He entirely agreed with Mr.Aveling's evidence on this point, and considered that the plan of repairing a crack by copper plugs was a dangerous one. The cracked piece of plate should have been cut out and a patch put on and secured by screwed studs or rivetting if it was possible to get in rivets. The stays should come through the new piece of plate. The patch should be of good size, as small patches never stood well. He considered that in the course of working at the ordinary pressure the crack in the firebox of the exploded boiler would have extended either quickly or slowly, and if quickly an accident possibly of a serious nature would have happened. Excepting this crack, and excepting also five stays which appeared to have been broken prior to the explosion, the boiler was in good condition. He had seen an engine of the same class as that which exploded draw a load of twice its own weight up the Star Hill at Rochester, but that was with the road in good condition; judging, however, from the evidence which had been given, and what had been said respecting the state of the roads, he was of the opinion that the engine which exploded had too great a load behind it at the time of the accident. He had witnessed the testing of some of the samples cut from the plates of the exploded boiler, and had come to the conclusion that the iron was of thoroughly good quality; it appeared, however, to have been somewhat hardened by the sudden manner in which the plates .had been flattened out. He considered that excessive steam pressure was the immediate cause of the explosion, and that this pressure was attained through the valves having been fastened down. He had formed a very strong opinion that the rupture commenced at the crack in the left-hand plate of the firebox; that this crack extended, releasing the centre row of vertical stays, and that the extra strain thus thrown upon the stays in the adjacent rows on each side caused them to fail in succession. The flat side of the firebox casing being thus deprived of the support of the firebox stays, the rupture of the shell would then commence, and the various plates give way in succession, the rips being of the irregular character so very generally found in cases of this kind. He did not consider that a pressure at all approaching 640lb. per square inch was necessary to cause the explosion owing to the condition of the firebox; but from the manner in which the backplate of the firebox had been bulged at points where the stays held, and from other indications, he considered that there must have been at the time of the explosion, or at some time previous, a pressure of over 250lb. or, possibly, 300lb. in the boiler.

Mr. Stenning asked him if the boiler would have exploded at 125lb. to which he replied that considering the state of the firebox it might in time have done so. He had never known a case in which copper studs had been used to such an extent. He was then asked if he had been influenced by the opinion of others. No, he replied, he had made an independent inspection of the boiler.

Lastly came William Weeks, proprietor of the engineering works and foundry on Waterside, Maidstone, who introduced himself simply as a millwright and engineer. He too had examined the safety valves and the burst boiler. The explosion was caused by overpressure of steam. The safety valves could be locked down. He considered the boiler, if in good condition, to have been fit for 100lb. pressure or even for 125lb. He agreed with the evidence of the preceding witness as to the cause of the explosion. Asked by Mr.Stenning if he had seen copper studs used for repairs he gave a rather dry affirmative. When asked whether he thought 500lb. pressure would have been needed to burst the boiler when new he again said no.

This concluded the evidence. After considering it for some two hours the jury returned to court about half past eight in the evening and returned this verdict:

1. We find that the deceased, Frank Underwood, met with his death by the explosion of the boiler of a traction engine belonging to Messrs.Jesse Ellis & Co., which explosion was caused by an excessive pressure of steam, and that the excessive pressure could not have been obtained unless the ferrules of the spring balances had been altered. We also find that the ferrules had been altered by the orders of Mr.Jesse Ellis, so that the men might be enabled to gain more steam.

2. We find that Martin is guilty of culpable negligence in not examining the engine when he took charge of it, and that the safety valves were locked between Wharf Lane and All Saints' Church by being screwed down, but by whom there is no evidence to show.

3. We find that the crack in the firebox was not properly repaired, and that Mr.Ellis is guilty of great negligence in allowing the engine to leave his works in such condition.

4. It is the opinion of the jury that the drivers of traction engines should pass an examination as to their capabilities, and that they should be provided with certificates of qualification, which they should be compelled to produce when asked to do so.

5. The jury recommended the compulsory use of safety valves that are the least likely to be tampered with.

6. The jury are of the opinion that the bye-laws respecting the removal of manure need not be altered.

7. The jury wish to express their approval of and belief in the evidence given by the witness Leadbetter.

As this verdict was one of manslaughter against Moses Martin the Coroner forthwith committed him on this charge.

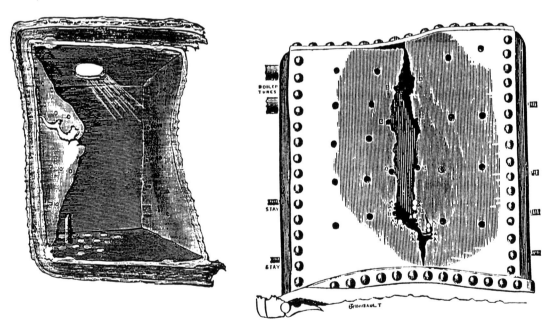

Figs 19 (left) and 20: Drawings showing the general view into the failed firebox, and the rip on the line of the old crack repaired with copper studding.

Chapter 7

THE TRIAL AND BEYOND

At the end of the inquest on December 22, 1880 when Moses Martin was told by the Coroner that he would be committed to the Assizes for trial on a charge of manslaughter he asked at once if he could be bailed. The Coroner declined on the ground that the granting of bail was outside his powers. It appears, therefore, that the accused man must have spent his Christmas in jail.

His trial took place before Mr.Justice Lindley on January 21, 1881, in the midst of a spell of snowy and bitterly cold weather. It seems probable that the Public Prosecutor must have had some doubts about the case as it was referred at the opening of the Assizes to the Grand Jury for a decision as to whether or not there was a case to answer to which question an affirmative was returned.

Mr.H.B.Deane was prosecuting counsel, Mr.Dickens acted for the defence, Messrs.Kingsford & Lawrie watched on behalf of Jesse Ellis & Co. and Mr.R.J.Biron for the Kent County Engine Owners' Association. The prosecution case was essentially a repeat of the evidence already given at the inquest by Tom Boarer, George Batey, W.H.Maw, Thomas Aveling and Jesse Ellis, no new matters of substance being introduced and it would be pointless to repeat it here. Maw reiterated his evidence that the pressure could not have been less than 300lb. per square inch, an opinion corroborated by Thomas Aveling. It became clear as the case proceeded that his Lordship was not impressed by the quality of some of the evidence.

When Mr.Dickens rose for the defence he announced that he intended to call no witnesses. His reply to the case put by the prosecution was this: the men knew they were allowed to screw down the safety valves to the ferrules and his client, Martin, had no means of knowing that the ferrules on the engine that exploded had been tampered with and shortened.

This plea was accepted by the Judge. In his summing up, clearly looking with favour upon the defence's points, Mr.Justice Lindley not only accepted what Mr.Dickens had said but went further. He questioned whether the valves had been screwed down at all as Boarer's evidence had been to the effect that when found after the explosion they were in the same state as when he had handed over the engine. As to the evidence of the overheard conversations he brushed this aside as worthless, mere repetition of beer talk. He could not accept, he said, the contention of the jury at the inquest that Martin had been culpably negligent in not checking the state of the safety valves on taking over the engine, nor could he acquiesce in the doctrine that having failed to exercise that extra care which hindsight had shown to be required he had thereby become criminally negligent, pointing out the higher degree of proof looked for in a matter of criminality as opposed to a civil action for damages.

After such a summing-up, so damning to the prosecution case and so obviously delivered in the belief that the defendant should not have been put on trial at all it is no surprise that the jury returned after no more than a token retirement to give a verdict of "Not guilty".

With the advantage of hindsight one is tempted to wonder why the coroner and his jury were so uncritical of the evidence given before them. The bombastic and often irrelevant evidence of Thomas Aveling was accepted en bloc, unchallenged in its deviation from the objectives of the inquest. Nor did any pounce upon the blatant absurdities of the answers given by Jesse Ellis himself whilst under cross-examination by the assessor. For the proprietor of a firm under his sole direction to answer the question "Was the boiler inspected by an independent engineer?" by replying "Not to my knowledge" was so farcical as to defy further comment.

It is equally perplexing that there was no comment upon the contradictory and evidently untruthful evidence of George Batey nor upon the way in which he had been intimidated during the court interval immediately before his cross-examination by

Mr.Stenning, during which he retracted much of what he had said earlier, in unequivocal terms, concerning the demerits of copper studding as a method of repair of cracking in the firebox plates.

Martin must have been intensely relieved by the verdict. Whether or not he was compensated for what he had been through is not known. Jesse Ellis may well have put his hand in his pocket to help him as he had done to others of his workmen in adversity.

As to the effects of the affair upon Jesse Ellis himself, in this, as in most other matters relating to his personal affairs I rely on the recollections of his daughter Mabel. At the actual time of the events she was only a few months old and recalled nothing of them directly. She had, however, in her late teens and early twenties, until she married, been very close to her father and,at the age of twenty-two, had been his companion on his second visit to Egypt. On the voyages out and home she had heard many of his reminiscences of his earlier life. That he was much affected by the death of Underwood has been noted already. This changed his attitude to safety and to standards of maintenance.

It had a serious financial effect upon the firm as well. The stained glass windows of All Saints' Church had been damaged by the blast and concern was felt about the effect of it on the organ. Whilst some of the glass was then relatively modern and capable of repair by native workmen, in the case of an antique window that was damaged it was expected that it would have to be removed and sent to Brussels for repair. As the total cost of the works was estimated to be over £500.00 the Churchwardens had taken legal advice on the issue of negligence by Jesse Ellis and had been advised that they would probably succeed in a case against the firm. Because, however, he was such a well-liked fellow townsman they hesitated to press him too hard. The debate in the Vestry meeting was lengthy and heated, some speakers wishing to make an example of him and others to temporise. It was a proposition of Mr.J.Monckton that resolved the matter. He proposed that Jesse Ellis & Co. should make a contribution of £250.00 towards the Vestry's costs, which the managing partner agreed to, probably gladly. Ralph Fremlin, brother-in-law of Jesse Ellis's partner, Marianne Fremlin, put in another £50.00 as a "good-will gesture".

How the damage to Clement's building was dealt with is not known. Mabel remembered the gouges in the brickwork being still visible many years later. By a peculiar coincidence the building was damaged by a second boiler explosion during the spell of intense cold in mid-January, 1881. A domestic boiler blew up, probably because the expansion pipe had frozen up, injuring several people including the son of Robert Elfick, Jesse Ellis & Co's traveller.

The engine involved, Aveling & Porter No.1302, was reconstructed after the accident. Jesse himself emerged from the affair a very much poorer - having carried, until then, no boiler insurance - but also a much wiser man, inculcated with a little of the humility that had been so absent before.

The question remains, what really happened early in the morning of December 3 ? It has always seemed to me that the verdict of the Assizes upon Martin represented justice and that only his lurid habits of speech had led to his being saddled with the blame in the first place. It had been established beyond doubt that the use of pressures in excess of the permitted maximum of 100lb. per square inch had been habitual amongst the drivers and condoned by the management. My own opinion, for what it is worth, is that Martin's explanation was the right one; namely that priming caused sticking of the valves and that the firebox, weakened by the bodged repair, gave way at a relatively low pressure.

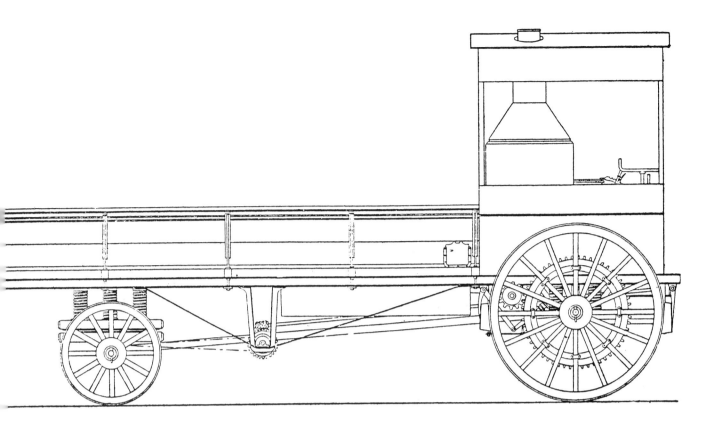

Fig 21: The second buck-wagon, designed to go with the driven wheels first, 1898.

Fig 22: The third design with driver and steersman separated once again, 1899.

Chapter 8

THE FIRST STEPS INTO WAGON BUILDING

Although Jesse Ellis had expended a great deal of energy in lobbying for the passage of the Locomotive Act 1896 his first effort in wagon building was not directed at the home market at all but at South Africa. Land transport in South Africa away from the railways depended heavily upon haulage by ox teams. Rinderpest, a disease of ruminants, virulent and usually fatal, had reached East and South Africa from Asia in the 1890's causing great depletion of draught oxen and creating a situation in which it was believed mechanical transport had a good chance of commercial success.

That an alternative to oxen as motive power was being looked for was probably understood amongst traction engine makers and engineers in touch with South Africa. In this general but undefined awareness Jesse Ellis would also certainly have shared. The clue to what may well have concentrated his attention upon it much more closely is the fact that A.G.W.Fremlin, a member of the family that had provided so much of the capital for the new firm, farmed near Ficksburg in South Africa. The beginning of the new company's involvement in steam wagon building was the making of three designs of heavy wagon aimed at the market there.

The first was patented by Jesse Ellis, using his private address at *Scraces, Barming*, on May 13, 1897 (Patent No.11901). Viewed in elevation it looked very much like a factory-made version of the traditional Boer ox-wagon. The basis was a braced steel channel underframe, with buffer beams front and rear for the full width of the chassis, carried on heavy wooden wheels with pressure plate hubs and steel axles. The leading axle had Ackermann steering. The vertical Field tube boiler was mounted at the rear and offset to the nearside. Above it, in a conical uptake, was the superheater. The engine was described as a "multicylinder reversible steam engine". From what can be discerned on the patent drawing it seems to have been a three cylinder radial, the horizontal shaft of which ran transversely across the vehicle, geared to a transverse countershaft, with change speed gearing and differential at the nearside end. Final drive was by two chains from sprockets outside the body of the vehicle to a large sprocket bolted to the wheels. Under the nearside centre of the lorry was what was described as "a condenser composed of corrugated sheets". Fuel was intended to be either liquid or solid. The firegrate was a fixed fireclay perforated slab and a removable solid slab, the purpose of which was to close the perforations in the fixed grate when running on liquid fuel. Fuel oil was carried in a cylindrical tank placed transversely under the frame at the extreme rear. Under the centre of the wagon, the carrying pin offset a little to the offside, was a horizontal winding drum, driven by an inclined shaft and double bevel gearing and clutches from the countershaft. This drum was to carry a wire rope to be used for "ascending steep hills, or for fording rivers or in conjunction with a crane post for lifting goods". There is no mention of coiling gear. This machinery and the goods carrying platform were within a waist-high wooden body of the type used for good class horse-drawn heavy vehicles. The load area was topped with wooden raves and a canvas or tarpaulin tilt.

The wagon was designed to be driven and steered from the rear and in order to make this possible the machinery area was roofed similarly but with the additional feature that to give forward vision a substantial wooden shelf, about a foot wide. was provided each side, borne on body irons and struts, so that its outer edge was roughly coincident with the outer edge of the driving wheel. From the outer edge of this the roof sprang giving room for a spectacle plate with plate glass windows to provide a view of the road ahead. The field of vision was about equal to that on a saddle-tank railway locomotive. No indication was given on the patent as to where it was intended to carry make-up feed water but a rectangular tank on the manstand seems likely.

The vehicle in its finished form differed a little in detail from the patent specification and drawings. The cylindrical oil tank was replaced by a shallow rectangular tank above the forecarriage but under the floor of the load area. The front buffer was omitted and instead a small steering seat and footplate was cantilevered forward with the steering wheel beside it on the offside, keyed to a short slanting shaft. For demonstration purposes the tilt was lettered "Colonial Motor Waggon, manufactured by Jesse Ellis & Co.Ltd., Maidstone, Kent, England". Later Ellis was to prefer to spell 'wagon' with a single 'g'. It is interesting to note that 'England' had been added in smaller letters on a separate line, as if an afterthought for the benefit of benighted colonials who might be ignorant of where Kent was situated.

Dimensionally the record of the machinery is a total blank although it is known that the wagon weighed about 5 tons empty and that the engine generated 25 IHP. In low gear the speed was three miles an hour and in high gear six to seven. The oil storage capacity was reported to be sufficient for about 50 miles of travelling.

The wagon must have been finished in December, 1897 to judge from the fact that an account of a test run appeared in *The Implement and Machinery Review* on January 1, 1898. The vehicle was demonstrated along the undulating London Road out of Maidstone, with a load of three tons. The reporter stated:

Well under control, it is easily manipulated, can be steered to a nicety and started or stopped instantly. As the trials took place on the high road in the middle of the day there was plenty of opportunity of noting how horses passed the wagon and in this respect all was satisfactory..................... The vehicle (is) destined for South Africa.

At this point the trail ends. Whether or not it was shipped to South Africa or who the intended purchaser might have been we simply do not know nor, over a period of about 25 years of searching, has it been possible to find out for sure. Purely as speculation the name of A.G.W.Fremlin is put forward. What we do know, however, is that by about May, 1898, a very much modified version of the wagon was in being, a circumstance that suggests that the original wagon had not lived up to the expectations of the builder.

The steering was once again managed from the manstand which remained over the driving wheels but it is clear that the wagon was meant to run with the driving wheels leading, and the steering axle at the rear. Instead of having Ackermann steering, this had reverted to the traditional form of 'front lock', with heavy coil springs between it and the main underframe – and working by chain and bobbin. The engine, too, was very different, a two cylinder vertical compound with a single piston valve controlling the steam admission and exhaust, actuated by a single eccentric reversing gear. The condenser had been moved to the cab roof and was described as "a patent atmospheric condenser provided with a fan driven from the engine". Special attention was said to have been paid to the gearing "which consists entirely of spur wheels, a chain being found unsuitable for such a heavy drive", surely a *cri du coeur* from experiences with its chain driven precursor. The driven axle was sprung with double coil springs each side, presumably, though it cannot be seen on the elevational drawing, in conjunction with an axle box and hornplates each side. The main drive gear was fixed to the wheel spokes and driven by a mating pinion on the overhung end of the countershaft. Braking was by blocks front and rear of the driving wheels, the rear pair hand operated by a handwheel via a slanting shaft and quick thread. The front pair were steam worked. The steam brake was said to be for emergency use. Oil and water were carried in tanks beneath the wagon. The winding drum, which had been a feature of the first wagon, was also used in the second. The wheels seem to have been of broadly similar pattern to those of the first wagon. The weight of the vehicle bore on the forecarriage (or perhaps one should call it the rearcarriage) through a ball race with phosphor bronze balls. The bodywork was a straightforward sided lorry, the cab a simple structure of sheet metal aprons, steel corner columns and a double roof to take the condenser.

This wagon, or one like it, must have been the one shown at the Royal Agricultural Society's Show at Birmingham in July, 1898, where it was catalogued merely as a 3 ton Colonial wagon and the price as "about £550.0.0." A description of it in *The Automotor and Horseless Vehicle Journal* of June, 1898, leaves no doubt that it was meant to go cab-first. By contrast the similar wagon shown at its native Maidstone when the

Royal was held there in 1899 undeniably had a steersman at the other end. A photograph survives of it thus and is reproduced. It was catalogued as a "Motor Buck Wagon, Colonial, Steam" and offered at £675.0.0.

It may thus be inferred, without absolute certainty, that three colonial wagons were made. Their respective fates are also lost in obscurity. It is possible, but non-proven, that two of them may have gone to South Africa as intended. As to the third some doubt exists if it ever left the county of Kent. Soon after my initial article on Jesse Ellis appeared in *Old Motor* in April, 1967, a letter arrived at the office of the magazine from the late George Eves who was born in Crockenhill, near Dartford, and once worked for the firm of Thomas Wood & Sons in the village. In it he describes having seen, as a small boy, a wagon broadly similar to the 1898 buck-wagon being demonstrated by Jesse Ellis to the directors of the Dartford Brewery Co., owners of a local pub in Crockenhill. He went on to say that it was bought by the brewery, reappeared the next week lettered in their name and worked for them for several years, driven by one Alf Long. The description he gave did not tally in every detail but it was, after all, the recollection by an old man of something that he had seen when he was a small child so one must not attach overmuch importance to that nor must one necessarily take his estimate of its working life to have been correct - a year seems an age to a six or seven year old. On the other hand one must not overlook either that old George loved to embroider a tale and was not above attempting a leg-pull, but the fact remains that I obtained my details from a source which, frankly, I think would not have been available to George and he could not have known them had he not seen the wagon. If it worked for the brewery at all I think it must have had a short life as it is very doubtful if it complied with the weight restrictions then in force and would, therefore, have laboured under the same restrictions as a traction engine.

At the 1899 Show at Maidstone Jesse Ellis exhibited a second wagon described as "a steam motor wagon for fruit, £450". The load capacity was rated as 2 tons and the speeds as 6 and 8mph respectively for the two gears. This was arranged in what was soon to become the conventional layout for an undertype wagon. A de Dion type vertical boiler was placed at the front of the wagon behind a simple steel apron. The chassis was of channel steel, the wheels of wood with steel tyres and pressure plate centre. It is not certain who supplied his wheels at this juncture but it may have been Bayleys of Newington Causeway, London. Later some wheels came from Stagg & Robson of Selby, who, I suppose, could have been the suppliers in this case. The wagon had a final drive by chain but how exactly the engine and gearing were arranged is not recorded. In the surviving photograph they can be seen to be encased in sheet iron. A conventional wooden body was fitted complete with raves and a canvas tilt extending over the driver's seat.

Jesse Ellis & Co ran this wagon themselves for about eleven months during which they stated, perhaps optimistically, that it covered about 2 000 miles. On May 31, 1900, it was sold to Fremlin Bros. and became their No 1. Their 'Motor Book' survived to be seen by me in 1967. The wagon ran with them for just over seven years and clocked up a mileage in excess of 40 000. With the introduction of registration in 1904 it became D442. Its owners dutifully provided the makers with testimonials of its prowess. Such testimonials were worth not very much at the best of times but since the Fremlin brothers were related to Marianne Fremlin, a major shareholder in Jesse Ellis & Co. Ltd, and were themselves both major shareholders and debenture holders, these were probably rather more prone to suspicion than most. Nevertheless the wagon, a prototype in the first instance, had a working life of five years and ran a substantial mileage so cannot be dismissed lightly.

This, the final wagon built by Jesse Ellis & Co. Ltd. in the last century, seemed to enjoy a measure of success but as it used roller chains in the final drive, a method of transmission against which the Managing Director had set his face firmly, all-gear drives were introduced in the new century despite the fact that the method of final drive used in the 1898 buck-wagons where the overhung drive gear fixed to the frame engaged with a driven gear able to move to the extent allowed by the springs had produced problems of binding and possible breakage of teeth. In the next seven years repeated efforts were made to wrestle with this puzzle, none ultimately successful.

Fig 23: The 1899 de Dion boilered wagon.

Fig 24:
The first double framed
wagon outside the Works
offices, June 19, 1901.

Fig 25:
The wagon on Detling Hill,
the same day.

45

The first to be explored was that worked out between Jesse Ellis and his draughtsman, J.F.Page, in their joint patent (No.12675) of June 17, 1899. In this the engine was carried on a subframe slung at the rear end below the main axle and at the front end by a central hanger, of which the bottom end engaged with a circular boss on the frame and the upper was forked to receive a lug on the main frame cross member to which it was secured by a pin, at right angles to the bottom boss. Later this idea was modified so as to provide a double frame system, a rigid lower frame unsprung and carrying the whole of the engine and gearing and an upper frame upon which the bodywork was mounted carried on springs from the lower frame. I have found no evidence that a wagon was actually completed on the patented engine frame system but the double frame method was used for the next wagon to be built which began a new era of construction.

Fig 26:
The wagon on Detling Hill,
showing the load carried.

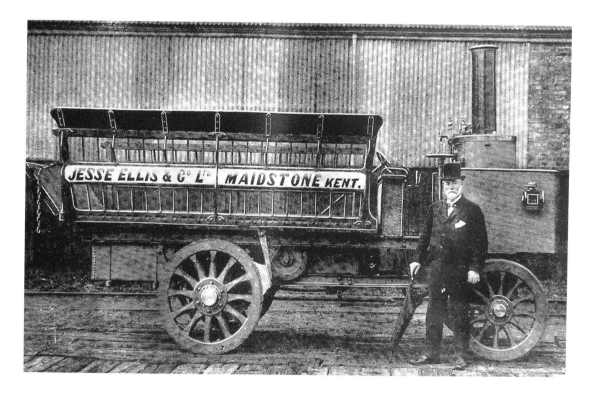

Fig 27: The 4-ton double framed wagon with millers bodywork.

Chapter 9

DOUBLE FRAMED WAGONS

The arrangement of the double framed wagon was patented on June 11, 1901, (Patent No.11937). The lower, partially sprung, frame was slightly narrower than the upper or sprung frame and was suspended directly upon the rear axle. On this frame were placed the boiler, engine and gearing. The wheels were artillery type with pressure plate hubs as before but smaller in diameter. The leading wheels were 3feet in diameter by 4inches across the tread; the driving wheels 3feet 6inches by 4½inches. Ackermann steering was fitted. The upper frame was carried onto the axles by hornblocks and spiral springs. The leading end of the lower frame was carried on the front axle by a multileaf flat spring. The boiler was described as of watertube type with about 4.9 square feet of grate area, and 75 square feet of heating surface, working at 200lb.per square inch, fired by a chute from manstand floor level and fed by an injector and by an eccentric operated pump driven off the countershaft. The engine, said to have developed 25 horse-power, was a straightforward compound with Stephenson valve gear, the cylinders 4inches and 8inches diameter by 6inch stroke. A simpling valve was provided to admit high pressure steam to the low pressure cylinder but with no separate exhaust for the high pressure cylinder as in the Foden simpling gear. The two speed gearing (to give speeds of 3 and 6mph) was all of steel, carried on the countershaft, the differential being on the main axle, which ran in roller bearings. A small flywheel was placed on the offside end of the crankshaft, carrying a foot-operated band brake, whilst a screw brake acted upon blocks bearing on the leading faces of the rear tyres. Overall the wagon was 16feet long and 6feet 6inches wide, with some 60 square feet of platform. It first appeared as a railed platform lorry with no cab other than a front apron plate and bunkers in front of the boiler.

Whilst the actual date of building is not known it was ready for a demonstration on June 19, 1901. Since Jesse was not one to blush unseen we may assume that it was then quite recently finished. The outing on which it was taken on that day began at Style's Medway Brewery at 11.35a.m. where it had been loaded with 15 barrels of beer, a 4½ gallon pin and two crates of bottled beer weighing in all 3 tons. The route was over Detling Hill to Sittingbourne and back, an overall distance of 24 miles. The outward journey took three hours, punctuated by two stops for oiling up and gear changes but coming back there were deliveries to be made and empties to collect so that it was five minutes to eight before the pioneers reached the brewery again. The route they had travelled included just under a mile of Detling Hill on which the maximum gradient was 1 in 6½ with lesser grades of 1 in 7½ and 1 in 10.

Subsequently a second wagon of this class appeared, showing minor differences from the first. The brake blocks, for instance, were to the rear of the driving wheels instead of in front of them, a step to the manstand was provided and the driver's seat was rearranged. A picture of it survives showing it at work for, or on demonstration to, S.P.Sanders, the Maidstone furniture remover. A third picture exists showing a wagon similar to that used on the Detling Hill demonstration but fitted with miller's bodywork and described as a 4-tonner. It is, of course, perfectly possible for these to have been the same wagon rebuilt or altered each time, but the balance of probability seems against this. A wagon like that working for S.P.Sanders formed the Jesse Ellis exhibit at the Crystal Palace Show in February, 1902, and there is a photograph extant showing one, also with the brake blocks behind the wheels, posing outside the Works House and office, bearing a street watering tank. In the press releases at the Crystal Palace Show it was stated that the exhibition wagon had been at work for some time. This would square with its having been the one used by Sanders. A company known as the London & Counties Distributing Co.Ltd. began a parcel service from London to Tunbridge Wells early in June, 1901, using two Bayley steam wagons. As a result of the Detling Hill demonstration on June 19, 1901, the wagon was given a trial by the London & Counties Co.

Fig 28:
A double framed
wagon with the
first design of
cross watertube
boiler.

Fig 29:
Double framed wagon
with the first
firetube boiler,
posed in St.Peters
Street, summer 1902.

Fig 30:
Double framed wagon,
(Provisional No.19) for
J.Batchelor & Son, 1903

Fig 31:
Wagon and three
trailers for India
Development Ltd.
(Prov.No.15)

Fig 32:
The wagon for
Clyde Engineering
(Prov.No.17),
fitted with second
type of firetube
boiler, 1903.

Fig 33:
The similar wagon
(Prov.No.18) for
Style & Winch,Ltd.
1903.

for fourteen days. At the end of that time they were so pleased with it that they took it over and gave the builders an order for five more. It is assumed that these were built and delivered, though in such matters one cannot be sure, but they have failed to surface in the initial registration of wagons in 1904. The explanation of this could be that registration was done with the London County Council who destroyed their early motor registration records. London & Counties made known their intention to begin a similar parcels service from London to Maidstone but this seems not to have happened.

Subsequent double frame wagons used either [a]:a firetube boiler covered by patent No.8522 of April 12, 1902, in which the shell was reduced in diameter at the waist and the smokebox tube plate was dished so that all tubes were fully submerged; [b]:a revised form of firetube boiler, patent No.8995, April 21, 1903, in which the upper and lower tube plates were coned and the firetubes were segmentally curved so as, it was hoped, to minimise leakage resulting from longitudinal expansion of the tubes; or [c]:the firm's later type of watertube boiler.

The first wagon to be fitted with the firetube boiler to the 1902 patent was that made for Jesse Ellis's second visit to Egypt in November, 1902. This adventure has been accorded a chapter to itself. Except for the boiler and the alternative wheels the wagon was very similar to the 1902 Crystal Palace wagon. The brake blocks fitted to the hand brake, however, had been made larger and longer, probably as a reaction to the short type having turned over in use. As a result of its being demonstrated successfully in Cairo and sold to the Egyptian Government, a second wagon was ordered, this time by the civil authorities for the Cairo Sanitary Administration. This wagon again had the first type of firetube boiler and was fitted with interchangeable bodies, the first of which was a wooden sided tipper with hinged raising boards and the second of which was a galvanized street watering tank with a sprinkler bar.

Both this wagon and the next to be supplied were on rivetted steel wheels with cast iron naves such as were used on traction wagons. The second wagon so fitted, a 5-tonner, was another export order destined for India Development Ltd, owners of Ottur Sugar Factory, Behar, Bengal. This, too, had the first type of firetube boiler. It had a longer wooden body with sides and hinged end and was accompanied by three low wheeled flat trailers with stake sides for sugar cane. The penultimate wagon to be supplied with the original design of firetube boiler was that sold to the Dartford Brewery Co.Ltd. in the spring of 1903. This was a draught beer dray with a low headboard and chock rails only, painted like a gipsy wagon with yellow and red body, the engine green and the wheels red. In January, 1904, this was registered D646. It had a short life with the Dartford Brewery possibly because of troubles with the boiler. It was returned to Jesse Ellis & Co. in early December, 1905, when it was repainted in dark green, lined in black and red and stayed there until sold on April 8, 1907, to Joseph Ford, the road roller owner and agricultural contractor at Winnersh, near Reading. Like other wagons for home use it had wooden artillery wheels with steel tyres.

By this time there were rumblings of trouble with the first design of firetube boiler, arising mainly from the expansion of the tubes leading to leakage at the tube plates. The wagons supplied in the second half of 1903 were all of the double framed type but were equipped with the curved tube type of firetube boiler patented on April 21 that year. One of these was exported to The Clyde Engineering Co. Ltd. who had works in Granville and Sydney, New South Wales and who were Australia's principal builders of railway locomotives. This had the traction wagon type of steel wheels as supplied on the example sent to India.

In June, 1903, a draught beer wagon with chock rails, side stanchions and chains was delivered to Style & Winch Ltd. (as Style's Brewery had recently become) at the Medway Brewery, a little way along St.Peters Street. This was painted blue and took Kent registration number D337. Not long afterwards a wagon was completed for J.Batchelor & Son of Ford Paper Mill, Little Chart, Ashford, Kent. Batchelors were celebrated for their blotting paper. It was recorded in the County Council's registration book as "flat for paper carrying or van" but the surviving photograph of it shows it carrying a fixed sided body. It may be, however, that this had been placed on it only for the purposes of the photographer as a very similar body appeared on other wagons. This wagon duly became

D330 on December 28, 1903. It was painted green, probably Jesse Ellis's favourite Brunswick green. Batchelors had it until July, 1914, when it passed to Charles Hooker of Boughton Lane, Loose, Maidstone. The last owner (on September 9, 1918) was Henry Farmiloe, Fir Lodge, Great Chart, near Ashford.

How long the Style & Winch wagon lasted is not known with precision. My informant on the life of it was Arthur McCaffery who drove one of the Fodens with which the brewery subsequently equipped itself. He did not know exactly how long it ran but, he said, it did not last very long after the Fodens came.

The final double frame wagon to be supplied in 1903 went to the Royal Arsenal Cooperative Society Ltd. of Woolwich, registered A78. This is recorded as having cylinders 4inches and 7inches in diameter by 7inch stroke. As it had a standard boiler the larger engine may have made it over-cylindered.

There then seems to have been a pause as the next wagon (D974) was not licensed until March 7, 1904. This was for Ellis's boiler suppliers, J.Balmforth & Co. of Luton. It had a flat body with iron standards, the sides and headboard two boards high and the stanchions joined by chains. Three four wheeled trailers with matching bodies were supplied with it and the whole group were painted blue with red wheels. The apron was lettered *Luton Motor Wagon Company*, suggesting that the purchasers had some idea of setting up in business as haulage contractors. Their interest proved to be short-lived, however, as the wagon was sold fifteen months later to the Tilehurst Haulage Co. in Berkshire. About this time the company supplied a wagon with a fixed van top to C.Hammerton & Co Ltd. of Stockwell brewery, London, other details of which have not survived. From photographs it was a wagon with double frame, resembling the others in the series, fitted with a firetube boiler of the first design.

Production appears to have settled down to the rate of about two or three a month as on April 6, Fremlin Brothers had a straightforward sided lorry, registered D1109. The livery in which this came out was chocolate lined in red for the body, green for the front apron and red for the chassis and wheels. The wagon completed at the end of the month, D1196, actually registered on April 27, was similarly painted with red chassis and wheels and dark green apron but in this case the body, a flat with low sides for carrying steel stock, was painted green also. The purchasers were Johnsons Iron & Steel Co. Ltd, Hall End Works, West Bromwich.

The following wagon had a fairly short time with its initial purchaser, John Williams & Co. the builders' merchants and slating contractors of Rotherhithe Street, London SE. They had it registered (D1250) on May 12, 1904, and it was back with its builders by March 27, 1906. This had a lorry body with hinged sides and end turned out with red chassis and wheels and yellow upper-work. It was re-sold on May 14 to Horace Summers & Sons, the Tunbridge Wells wholesale fruiterers and greengrocers for whom it was repainted in dark green lined in red and yellow, a livery that was to be their standard until the firm was wound up nearly seventy years later.

Time was beginning to run out both for the double frame and for the firetube boiler. Though the curved tubes and dished tube plates of the second design of firetube boiler solved the problem of leakage from the tube ends, the boiler as a whole was not a prolific producer of steam, its troubles compounded by the length of steam pipe from the boiler to the engine steam chest and by the absence of an effective superheater. A soundly designed superheater yielding hot, dry steam was to be one of the salient points of the successful Sentinel undertypes. I knew Charles Hooker who drove the Ellis wagon fitted with this type of boiler, which belonged to his father. His judgement was that for jogging round a town or city or for short hauls between, say, a factory and goods station it might have sufficed, but that for continuous work over longer distances and especially for hill climbing a more effective source of steam was required. This was tackled in two ways as we shall see in the next chapter.

The double frame added to the unladen weight yet at the same time it did not entirely succeed in its objective of keeping the gearing in truth. Mostly this fault seemed to manifest itself in the shearing of the bolts that held the countershaft bearing brackets in place but it must also have contributed to wear.

At the 1904 Royal Show, held in London, three exhibits were shown with the double frame. There was a bare chassis with the new watertube boiler, a steam bus, to which we will return later, and a "sanitary tipping and street watering van". The first named was sold at the Show to a representative of Barraud & Abrahams who were agricultural merchants at Palmerston North, in New Zealand. This had the patent watertube boiler and was fitted with wider wheels than standard so as to fit it for traversing stubbles. It had a dropsided body with hinged raising boards.

The sanitary wagon was sold some weeks after the Show to Maidstone Corporation. Mr.Bunting, the Borough Surveyor, was authorised to make the purchase by a minute of August 24, and the wagon was registered (D1561) in the Corporation's name on August 31, 1904. The livery was primrose for the upper work and red for the frame and wheels. The Borough Council minutes chronicle its adventures, or misadventures. It was repaired by Ellis in January,1906, August,1907 and January,1908, whilst the firm supplied a set of new tubes in July,1908. Presumably these last three transactions were with Jesse himself in his separate establishment at Allington Forge. Within a space of sixteen months the tank was twice replaced, the first time by Pontifex at a cost of £16.0.0. but the second time the cost was £22.0.0. from G.A.Harvey of Woolwich. Other repairs noted are a visit to Drake & Fletcher of Maidstone in October,1909, which cost the Council £43.0.0. and in January, 1911, (£11.0.0.). In May,1913, the wagon was recorded as "broken down" and it cost £20.0.0. to get it going again.

Probably the last double framed wagon to be sold by the firm was that which went to E. & H.Kelsey of Culverden Brewery, Tunbridge Wells on August 24, 1904, and was registered D1551. By some curious mischance it was first entered in the Heavy Motor Car register as a "Blake". The wagon was fitted with a typical brewery body, the lower sides close-boarded and the upper open-railed. Kelsey's livery for vehicles was very dark green with red chassis and wheels, the lettering in gold leaf. They ran the Ellis wagon until early in 1909 when it was taken in part exchange by Wallis & Steevens for one of their overtypes. It is likely, however, that it never left the town as on February 26 it passed to the nearby High Brooms Brick & Tile Co.

It does seem probable that at least one further street cleaning and watering wagon on a double frame was built for stock and remained unsold. This was disposed of by the Receiver and is discussed later.

Fig 34: Wagon (Prov.No.31),double framed, with second type of firetube boiler, 1904.

Fig 35:
Wagon
(Prov.No.21) for
J.Balmforth &
Co. of Luton,
double framed
with second type
of firetube
boiler.

Fig 36:
Wagon for
Dartford Brewery
Co.Ltd, 1903,
double frame,
first type of
firetube boiler,
(Prov.No.16).

Fig 37:
Prov.No.22, a
double framed
wagon with the
first design of
firetube
boiler, 1904.

53

Figs 38 - 42 (anti-clockwise)
Wagons Provisional Nos.20,26,
24,23, and 32. All are double
framed, except the latter
which, incidentally, was used
by Fremlins until 1920.

Fig 43:
Prov.No.30,
(1904),the
double framed
street watering
and tip wagon
with the second
design of
firetube boiler.

Fig 44:
The single
framed tipper
(Prov.No.33)
for Hajee
Ismael Sait
1904. The
boiler is the
second design
of crossed
watertube.

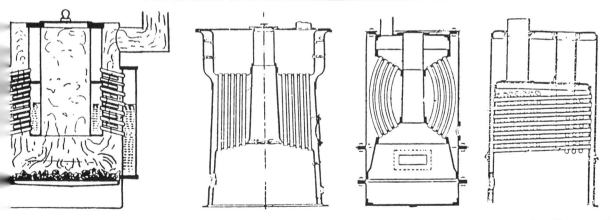

Fig 45: Boiler cross-section sketches, left to right, the de Dion type, the first and second vertical firetube types and the second design of crossed watertube.

Chapter 10

SINGLE FRAMED WAGONS and OTHERS

The Heavy Motor Car Order that came into force on September 1, 1905, limited the tare weight of heavy vehicles to 5 tons.This placed the double framed wagons at a further disadvantage. They already suffered the twin problems of high unsprung weight and an unladen weight that consumed too high a proportion of the total permissible weight. The new rules forced the abandonment of the double frame.

The problem before the Ellis designers, therefore, was of devising a suitable alternative without resorting to the use of roller chains which, by definition, were anathema. Thornycroft, another maker dedicated to an all gear drive, solved a similar dilemma by phasing out altogether the manufacture of steam powered vehicles in which, up to that time, they had enjoyed considerable success.

At Invicta Works Jesse Ellis (jun.) approached the situation in another and less dramatic way. The engine unit was moved off-centre to the off-side. This permitted an Oldham coupling to be introduced into the first shaft enabling the chain of gears in the final drive to follow more nearly the movement of the rear axle whilst allowing the engine crankshaft to be rigidly aligned with the frame. Since this arrangement remained adequate only for limited relative movement of the frame and axle the further precaution was taken of inserting a Stevens patent spring bar into the rear suspension, an invention of Jesse Ellis's near neighbour, W.A.Stevens, by which a compensating action was introduced between the two suspension points of the axle, intended to keep the rear axle more nearly in parallel with the frame. A new company, of which Jesse Ellis became a director, was formed to exploit the Stevens spring bar.

The prototype wagon incorporating the new ideas was a sided lorry exhibited at the Crystal Palace Show in February, 1904, and again at the Royal in July, and registered on July 23, 1904, as D1496. Jesse Ellis turned the wagon out in his standard livery of green lined in yellow for the cab with red chassis and wheels but the lorry body was in varnished hardwood. This also had the firm's revised design of watertube vertical boiler patented on July 31, 1903, (No 16818). A year after the Royal Show this wagon was sold to Fremlin Brothers. The second wagon known to have been designed with the new features was that sold in April, 1904, to Hajee Ismail Sait of Bangalore, India. To a limited extent Fremlin Brothers may be looked upon as a captive client because of the family's capital interest in the firm. Powerful though this incentive may have been, it cannot have been the only explanation of Fremlins' use of Ellis wagons - the wagons themselves must have had intrinsic merit. The Fremlin partners went on to buy two further wagons. They were D2393, the 2-tonner shortly to be described, and D2891, another single framed wagon with watertube vertical boiler.

All had relatively long lives. D1496 was not taken out of service until 1920 when it was sold to T.King of Maidstone for £60.0.0. The last was D2891 which continued until 1927 when, with some reluctance, the firm parted with it to James, a scrap metal merchant in Wyatt Street, Maidstone, for £4.0.0. This had had a sympathetic driver, Wally Cruttenden, who had learned to live with its idiosyncrasies. Employed on local deliveries in the town and environs its furthest trip was normally to Aylesford, about 3 miles, except at hop-picking times, September and early October, when it ventured as far as the *Bluebell* at Beltring managing two trips a day, a total of some 32 miles. Wally reckoned to leave the brewery with a clean fire and a full head of steam. As far as the tram depot at Barming it was steady work on the collar. Thereafter the route levelled out and then fell as far as Teston where there was a short hill followed by a stretch of level and a drop down through Wateringbury to the west side of the Medway bridge after which there was a short rise and a relatively easy run from there through Nettlestead and Hale Street to Beltring. Forty years later he still recalled the wagon with some affection. Realist enough to know it was not perfect he reckoned, nevertheless, that it was quite capable of a useful day's work, a view confirmed by Mr.H.W.(Bert) Standen, from the management side. He said it was withdrawn in the end because the company did not consider its life potential justified the expense of converting it from steel tyres to solid rubbers to conform to the changed requirements of the Construction and Use Regulations.

Had the designer incorporated an effective superheater into the steam generating arrangements the performance of these latter wagons would have been much enhanced but the experience of attempting to use superheat, like that of the single eccentric valve gear, on the buckwagons appears to have decided the issue against both for good. Without a good superheater even the watertube boiler seems to have failed wholly to satisfy the firm's expectation for though the next wagon to appear, registered D1688 for the Royal Arsenal Cooperative Society Ltd. at Woolwich on January 11, 1905, was fitted with a watertube boiler there were already plans for producing a wagon with a locomotive boiler. Contemporaneously the firm were also building a 2-ton model which was unveiled to potential purchasers at the Crystal Palace Show in February, 1905. This is likely to have had a watertube vertical boiler but one cannot be certain. It seems to have been subjected to testing and alteration as it was not registered until March 5, 1906, over a year later, when it became D2393. Later that month Fremlins bought it, as we have seen, using it for bottled beer deliveries from their South-east London depot in Danes Road, Camberwell. The first wagon fitted with a locomotive boiler was also intended for Crystal Palace. In this the frame remained very much as in the vertical boilered wagons with the boiler barrel kept high. No details survive of the exact method of attachment but the firm were careful to state that it was of their own design and, by inference, therefore not derived from Foden's patent. A basic problem arising from the high pitched boiler was forward visibility but, for the time being, nothing was done about this. When shown it had one piece cast steel road wheels similar to those used on Garretts' first undertype wagon. Garretts obtained their wheels from Krupp of Essen. It is not impossible that the Ellis wheels were from the same manufacturer. The bodywork was a drop-sided lorry. The bunkers were arranged on either side of the barrel at the front and stoking was by way of a vertical chute through the firebox crown, a method adopted also by, *inter alia*, Bretherton & Bryan. This wagon was eventually registered D1822 on April 11, 1905, for the Dartford Brewery Co. Ltd. and painted brown, presumably with the usual red chassis and wheels.

A second, and essentially similar, wagon was licensed by Jesse Ellis & Co. as D1803 on April 5, 1905. After a round of visits to the shows of that season it was sold on August 8 to Charrington & Co. Ltd, Wellington Brewery, Gravesend. This wagon was painted in the same style as the previous one.

In September, 1906, a 5-ton tipper was sold to Hajee Ismail Sait, already a customer for a single frame wagon with watertube boiler in April, 1904. Whereas the first wagon was shipped to him at Bangalore, the second was sent to him at the English Warehouse, Kolar Goldfield, Mysore. Whether this one had a vertical or a horizontal boiler is not known.

On December 12, 1905, the firm registered a wagon with the watertube vertical boiler as D2270 for their own use. The exact type of body is uncertain - it is described merely as "wagon". The colour was chocolate lined in red and black. In February 1906 it was sold to William Miller of Berkswell House, Coventry, but on July 15 the following year it went to William Nayler, Woodsellon Lodge, Sedgley, Staffordshire.

There followed D2672 (July 2, 1906) a tipper with watertube boiler first taxed by the firm in their own name and sold by the Receiver in October, 1907, to Percy H.G. Powell-Cotton of Quex Park, Birchington, Kent, creator of the remarkable museum of stuffed animals that is still to be seen there. This was dark red. Powell-Cotton sold it on April 23, 1915, to Basingstoke Gas Co., in which the Wallis family (of Wallis & Steevens) had a substantial stake. Repairs to the wagon were done at Wallis & Steevens' North Hants Ironworks from time to time, including making and fitting a new crankshaft. Like Fremlins' wagon D2891, its final demise in 1927 was the result of the virtual prohibition of steel tyres. Picking its way round Basingstoke with loads of coke and running on a fuel so cheap and plentiful in the gasworks as hardly to be taken into account, it gave its owners reasonable satisfaction.

Fig 46: The first design of locomotive boilered 4-ton wagon, (prov.No.36).

Figs 47 and 48: Charringtons had the loco boilered wagon (D1803) in 1905 (Prov.No.37), but some months afterwards an advertisement appeared showing a vertical boilered wagon for the same customer, with the identical registration, a problem discussed in Chap.15.

Fig 49: The 2-tonner
with epicyclic gear
box as it appeared
at Olympia in 1907.
            and
Fig 50: As it was in
its later years when
working for Arnolds
of Branbridges,
East Peckham, Kent.

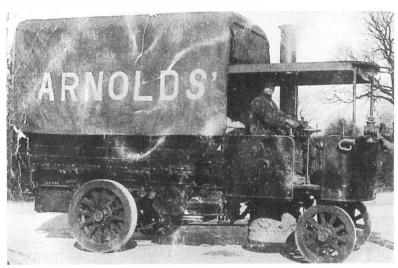

Fig 51:
The locomotive
boilered 6-tonner
of 1907.

The wagon registered on January 30, 1907 (D2979) for Richardson & Co. of Marjory Lane, Durham, was a vertical boilered (presumably watertubed) wagon with a lorry body, and fixed canvas tilt, the lorry in standard green, probably with red frame and wheels and the tilt top white.

By this time the financial affairs of the company were nearing crisis point but this did not inhibit the development of new designs, perhaps in the hope that by pulling off a spectacular advance it might stave off this increasing stringency in the money supply.

In time for the 1907 show at Olympia two fresh types of steam wagon were made. The first, and in many ways, the most interesting of these was a redesigned 2 tonner. It will be remembered that when the manufacture of the 2 ton chassis was resumed early in 1906 only one example (D2393) was sold. That which appeared in the opening weeks of 1907 was an altogether more sophisticated machine than anything attempted before. The vertical boiler (probably firetube) was moved to the back of the cab with the fuel bunkers on either side, the seats for the driver and mate above them. This boiler seems to have been one of the exhibition boilers taken around Royal and other shows, and here being thriftily used up. Intended for a much larger wagon it dominated the cab area and, because of the smaller need of steam in this wagon, may not, for once, have embarrassed the driver by the want of it. A plain curved apron enclosed the front of the manstand. As exhibited the body was a plain flat lorry with chock-rails. The engine remained a conventional cross-compound but the three speeds (1¾, 2¾ and 6m.p.h.) were arranged by the use of a Fairfax epicyclic gearbox in which all the gears were constantly in mesh. Hitherto the driver had had to stop his wagon, dismount and crawl underneath in order to change gear. In the new arrangement he could do it from the manstand with less bother than with many of the contemporary petrol-engined lorries. The Fairfax gearbox had been developed by J.S.Fairfax & Co. Ltd, Chiswick, London, who at the same period made the Fairfax motor car. Amongst Fairfax's clients was the London Power Omnibus Co. who had six of his gearboxes. He was reported at one time to be also preparing designs for a gearbox suitable for a 5 ton steam wagon though for whom is not known. Possibly it was for Jesse Ellis & Co.Ltd. had the firm not closed down. Tantalisingly the details of the final drive of this 2-ton wagon have not survived.

Although the wagon was photographed for *The Autocar* carrying a load of whisky boxes belonging to the firm of W.Anderson & Co.Ltd. of London and Glasgow it had not been sold to them or to any other purchaser by the time the Receiver entered into possession. It was, however, sold before the disposal sale to Summers & Son, the Tunbridge Wells wholesale fruiterers, who had had an earlier wagon. At the time of its first registration as D3457 on September 5, 1907, it was painted in red and black, supposedly red chassis and wheels and black upperwork, but it is likely that Horace Summers changed the black to his usual dark green. After two years he sold it, in October, 1909, to W.Arnold & Sons, the millers and traction engine proprietors at Branbridges, East Peckham, Kent. For their part they ran it for several years until in August, 1917, it passed into the hands of George Harper, a boiler and machinery dealer who had a yard opposite Chiswick Park station in Middlesex. There the trail is lost.

The second wagon built at the same time was a development of the horizontal boilered wagons, designed to carry six tons. In this Ackermann steering was replaced by chain and bobbin, a retrograde step,but in other respects, barring the continued absence of superheat, it was a neat and well finished machine. The top firing was replaced by a firedoor in the conventional position, necessitating the moving of the back of the cab about three feet towards the rear. This enabled a coal bunker astride the boiler to be used. The apron plates were arranged rather as on a Foden, giving space for a tool locker at the extreme front on one side and an oil bottle locker on the other. It had Stagg & Robson's recently patented composite wheels in which pressure plate hubs were combined with wooden spokes and a steel rim with pockets instead of wooden felloes to receive the outer ends of the spokes. A very stylish cab roof cambered in both longitudinal and transverse planes enhanced the appearance compared with the older roofs but in practice it did little for the driver. On wet days the water was carried to the two front corners of the roof where it ran off and was blown back over the driver and mate.

When the firm closed it was still in stock. An unrealistic price was put on it at the dispersal sale and as a result the Receiver was left with it on his hands where it became steadily more of an embarrassment. Whilst it is not known what reserve he had had in mind it is known that all he got for it when he sold it in the end was £175.0.0. The sale was dated March 7, 1910, but the wagon must have needed work on it as it was not registered (as D5058) until May 8. The colour was noted merely as "red" and the purchasers were S.C.Gilson & Sons of Holcombe near Bath. They had nearly ten years of use from it before selling it to Charles Gunter of Waterside Farm, Thatcham near Newbury, on March 30, 1920.

Besides this wagon three others were in the sale. Two of these were combined slop carts and watering wagons and the third was the steam bus. One street watering vehicle was the double framed wagon built for stock and never sold. This was bought by Jesse Ellis and Richard Crosby for their venture at Allington and was sold with their other rolling stock on September 21, 1910. On the evidence of Fremlin Brothers "Motor Book" this was purchased by them to be broken up for spares. The second was another example with watertube vertical boiler of which a photograph survives. Though this was a potentially saleable wagon it took some eighteen months for the Receiver's pride to become reconciled to a realistic price. It went for £150.0.0. on May 4, 1909, supposedly minus tank and sprinklers, to Samuel Atherton, owner of Hanwood Collieries near Shrewsbury, having been registered D4411 the day before. This went away painted chocolate lined in black.

At the 1907 Olympia Show the company broke new ground in another respect beyond the two steam wagons for they also had on their stand a 14/16h.p. petrol engined chassis intended to be fitted with a van body for 15 to 20cwt. payload. Powered by a four cylinder engine, of provenance unknown, it had the speed change arranged through the French Fouillaron system of expanding and contracting pulleys in conjunction with a leather link belt. Fouillaron, the inventor of the transmission system, who had a works at Levallois-Perret, Seine, had been making motor cars with this form of transmission since 1900 and continued to do so until the business folded in 1914 but always with proprietary power units. Widespread acceptance eluded him, however. Nothing is known of the chassis shown by Jesse Ellis & Co, neither how far it was their own work nor how much of it was imported material from Fouillaron. It had been disposed of, supposedly by sale to a customer, before the Receiver entered into possession of the firm but thereafter sight of it is lost.

One wagon remains unidentified. In its report of the Olympia Show in its issue of April 1, 1907. the *Implement and Machinery Review* reported that an Ellis wagon had been sold to a purchaser in Valparaiso. One may conjecture that it was the locomotive boilered slop cart and street watering wagon that was on the firm's stand at the 1906 Olympia show but it seems unlikely that we shall ever know that with certainty.

Fig 52: The Egyptian wagon, on its normal wheels, posed with Jesse (left), George Winter and Frank Stohwasser before it was shipped.

Chapter 11

THE ADVENTURE IN EGYPT

There can be no denying that Jesse Ellis and his eldest son were fascinated by Egypt. Not only is this demonstrated by their actions but confirmed directly by Mabel White. Father and son were very close to one another, keeping up a correspondence while Jesse (jun.) was at Aswan on both the general aspects and the terrain of Egypt and the Sudan and the readiness of the area for the introduction of mechanical road vehicles. They paid great attention also to the problems created by the arrival in Africa of rinderpest and the depredations of the disease amongst draught oxen.

Of the father's first visit to Egypt we know relatively little. What is known has been related already. When it came to his second visit, however, the picture is somewhat different. Mrs.Ellis had no wish to go with him on either journey but when he was planning his second visit he asked his daughter Mabel if she would like to accompany him. She accepted eagerly and remembered it vividly sixty-five years later.

The visit was tied up too with another venture as well as his own. Probably as a result of his past activities as Farrier Quartermaster Sergeant in the West Kent Yeomanry he had made the acquaintance of Francis Joseph Stohwasser and George Birchnell Winter. Frank Stohwasser was a maker and supplier of puttees and other military clothing and had, it seems, a very substantial business. George Winter was a former regular soldier. He had been galloper to Lord Chesham (Charles Compton William Cavendish) in South Africa in 1900. A galloper in a cavalry regiment was the equivalent of a runner in the infantry, a trusted bearer of his officer's messages to his subordinates and by inference a thoroughly reliable man with plenty of personal courage and initiative. On leaving the Army Winter had joined Stohwasser's business which had a head office at 39 Conduit Street, London W.1. In April, 1901 it was turned into a limited company with a capital of £40 000.0.0. and the grandiloquent title of the Stohwasser & Winter Puttee Legging and Military Equipments Corporation Ltd.

George Winter had devised a *desert wagon*, a four wheeled steel framed vehicle on broad tyred steel wheels with wire tension spokes. In pockets along its sides it carried the canvas of a large tent which, its inventor claimed, could be erected in a matter of minutes. In other words it was the progenitor, on a massive scale, of the trailer tent. Winter believed that this might have potential for military use in Egypt and the Sudan.

Between them he and Jesse Ellis put together a scheme to combine their two burning preoccupations into a single venture. Jesse Ellis was well regarded by the officers of the Yeomanry and doubtless George Winter enjoyed the patronage of Lord Chesham. Mabel was vague as to how the invitation to demonstrate the wagons was obtained though she thought it might have been through these connections but the ground had undoubtedly been prepared by the work done by traction engines in the South African War, by the results of the War Department Trials in 1901 and by the stated belief of Lord Kitchener, when Commander-in-Chief, that progress in Egypt away from the railways depended upon the introduction of mechanical road transport.

The steam wagon sent was of the double frame pattern with the first design of firetube boiler. Several photographs exist of it as a demonstration vehicle. In the autumn of 1902 the work was begun of converting it to "desert" specification. It was fitted with a large canvas tilt top extending over the driving seat, painted white and lettered *Egyptian Steam Motor Wagon, manufactured by Jesse Ellis & Co.Ltd, Maidstone, Kent,England, in conjunction with Stohwasser & Winter Corporation Ltd, London.* A set of steel alternative wheels was ordered having 6inch wide tyres at the front and 9inch at the rear, 3feet and 3feet 6inches diameter respectively, in which flanges were provided to each side of the wheel to minimise lateral movement in soft sand. The boiler was fitted with a paraffin burner and a cylindrical fuel tank was mounted under the offside of the manstand. Unfortunately we do not know the burner system used. Although the buckwagons had had roof condensers no attempt was made to fit condensing apparatus to this wagon.

After the customary photographs it was shipped from London on November 11. The ship was scheduled to call at Gibraltar on its way round to Marseilles, where it docked conveniently close to the Gare Maritime. The Ellises and George Winter did not travel with it, preferring to avoid the discomforts of an autumn voyage through the Bay of Biscay but instead crossed from Dover to Calais, making their way by train to Marseilles and thence with the ship to Alexandria. At Alexandria the wagon and trailer were put onto rail for Cairo. This operation took several days and the delay chafed upon Jesse Ellis who even at fifty-eight still had plenty of his old impatience. As he remarked in a letter to Richard D.Crosby, the company secretary, "We keep moving along but we find by experience that there is no such thing as being in a hurry in Egypt."

The party went ahead of it to Cairo where they stayed at Shepherd's Hotel. Since Cairo was full of visitors for the impending opening of the Aswan Dam the prices had gone up accordingly to Jesse Ellis's annoyance. On Thursday, November 27, the day he began his letter to Crosby, Jesse received a note from Col.Friend and the Sirdar, Sir Reginald Wingate, saying that they would call upon him on Saturday, "so we hope" he wrote, perhaps with resignation, "to see the wagon tomorrow." He went on:

"We have driven out some five or six miles in the desert, where the preliminary trial is to take place, and as the going is much better than I expected, I think we shall be able to run the wagon alright. I shall also get them to try it up to the Citadel, which lies on a hill in the centre of Cairo. It is a good road but steep, having a gradient of about one in seven, like Buckland Hill. There is a lot of talk about the trials and if we have good luck they mean us to go up to Khartoum, though I hope not, as it would take us a long time, and they are sticking up the prices to a ruinous level, on account of the people who have come to see the opening of the Dam. If, however, we do go to Khartoum it will mean a big order."

He soon discovered that the way to accelerate the pace of Egyptian labourers was an application of baksheesh. From the instalment of this marathon letter written the following day it is clear that he had enlisted some dependable local help.

"We have been hard at work getting the wagon off at the station. If Mr.Winter and I had not been here it would have taken about a month. We are now waiting for lunch, quite tired and fainting. We have arranged with our dragoman to be back at the station at four o'clock, as we hope to have the wagon out before dinner. We also hope to find it intact, as they are not at all particular how they drop things about, and if we had not been there they would have thought nothing of letting the motor drop from a crane with a bang but one has to keep paying baksheesh and then you can get on."

Later he wrote another paragraph in his saga:

"We have been out to the station again and intended to get our wagon out. But, oh no! This is Rama day and they were all feeding as soon as the sun set and they tell us that as this is their Sunday and they never work after two o'clock we have done wonders today. So far we are lucky.

Mr.Cockburn and his friend left here tonight for Aswan but we have to see Colonel Friend this (coming) morning and if the first trial is successful we shall have to go to Khartoum. One such journey is quite enough as it is anything but a pleasure. I have just been told that it must have been my persuasive powers that caused the Arabs to work as they did today. We still have got a lot of things to get up but they say they want twenty-four hours notice for everything."

Notwithstanding his exasperation and his misunderstanding of the nature of Ramadan and of the Muslim significance of Friday as a day of prayer, Jesse Ellis and George Winter, aided by the dragoman, were successful in getting their vehicles back into their hands without damage. The private viewing by the Sirdar and Colonel Friend went off in a cordial atmosphere. The Sirdar reiterated the view that mechanical road transport was a necessity if Egypt was to develop. Doubtless this was a platitude he used at every meeting with an interested person but Jesse Ellis felt suitably encouraged. In a more practical vein the Sirdar issued instructions that he (Ellis) was to be provided with whatever assistance he required.

The first trial through which the steam wagon was put was the ascent of the

Citadel Hill on Tuesday December 2. For this it was loaded with 3 tons of ballast, probably a juncture at which its owner appreciated the services of the squad of Egyptian soldiers assigned to him, as he had no help of his own apart from Winter and the hired interpreter. He steamed up the wagon and drove it himself. His apparel for the day was a blue serge suit, white kid gloves and a hard felt hat - this in a temperature of perhaps 80°F in the shade. An excited Cairene crowd followed the wagon through the streets toward the Citadel. As it passed Shepherd's Hotel the guests lined the windows. Some photographed its progress.

As the climb through the narrow winding streets of the Citadel Hill began Jesse Ellis necessarily put the wagon into slow speed. This, in turn, made it easier for the crowd to keep up with it and correspondingly more difficult for the driver to avoid the importunate individuals who persisted in putting themselves in danger. With its test load the wagon climbed the hill in fourteen minutes without needing to stop. Jesse Ellis and George Winter considered it a satisfactory performance. The return trip the next day was made without incident or injury to the crowds who beset the wagon as fiercely as on the way up and whose self-imperilling attempts to run with it and touch it brought them into conflict with their more static fellow citizens as well as threatening to put them under the wheels.

The wagon was then taken out to the Army barracks at Abbasieh where the regular wheels were changed for the set of broad tyred desert wheels. No doubt at this point Messrs Ellis and Winter again appreciated the services of their squad of soldiers. For a first test the wagon was loaded with forty-one soldiers and coupled to the desert tent wagon with which it was sent 2½ miles down the Suez road. This was accomplished in good order.

Once out in the desert, however, the inspecting officers asked Jesse Ellis to take it through loose drift sand. Where the loose sand overlaid a firm surface it progressed fairly well but where the drifts were deep and effectively bottomless it could make little progress. Whilst at Abbasieh the working of the tent wagon was demonstrated, apparently with satisfaction, but what became of it I do not know.

Sir Reginald Wingate, Commander-in-Chief of the Egyptian Army, was at Khartoum but the officers who had witnessed the trials on his behalf, Colonels Friend and Peake, telegraphed their favourable findings to him. The reply was an acceptance of the wagon and an instruction to send it to him at Khartoum. Mabel did not go with it but instead visited her brother at Aswan so we know nothing about that part of the enterprise. The Government bought the demonstration wagon but did not, contrary to Jesse Ellis's hopes, place orders for any more for military use though he did succeed in getting an order from Sir Horace Pinchin, the head of the Sanitary Department of Cairo, for a sanitary and street watering wagon. Sadly for Ellis this was not repeated.

Though as a commercial proposition the visit to Egypt had on balance to be rated a failure, for the Ellises, father and daughter, it had been a tremendous social success. The military establishment in Egypt made a great fuss of them. Contrary to what is sometimes imagined it was not staffed by Blimps. Friend and Peake were both in their thirties and very personable men. A number of the officers were keen on motor cars and though Jesse Ellis did not own a car himself he was thoroughly conversant with what was happening in France and Great Britain in the motoring field. Although Mabel never admitted to flirting with any of the young officers in Cairo clearly she had enjoyed their company. Besides this she had had a most interesting time with her brother at Aswan with all the advantages of being an insider and of seeing aspects denied to mere spectators. The sea voyage in both directions had also been an interesting experience resulting in meeting some diverting characters including a couple who either did not, or professed not to, believe that Jesse was Mabel's father but rather that he was a middle-aged roué indulging himself with a young girl.

The tour gained the firm useful notices in the press. The *Sunday Times* gave it three paragraphs, and it found its way besides into the *Express* and *African World.* Whether or not Stohwasser & Winter's tent wagon gained any commercial or military use seems doubtful. A specimen, or perhaps even the one shown in Egypt, was on the Ellis stand at the Royal Show in 1904, but it appears never to have been taken up by the

British Army. Enquiries have not revealed what became of the two wagons in Egypt. It seems unlikely now that we shall ever know. Frank Stohwasser and George Winter and their company prospered for some years but about the middle of the 1914-18 war the company faded away and was wound up in 1922.

Fig 53:
The wagon on the Suez road, Jesse driving and George Winter in the foreground, loaded with some of their Egyptian military helpers.

Fig 54:
On test at Abbasieh with the desert tent wagon behind.

Fig 55:
The wagon ordered by the Cairo Sanitary Administration.

Chapter 12

STEAM BUSES and LIGHT RAILWAYS

Jesse Ellis was the operator of ragstone quarries at Boughton Monchelsea. The site was to the south of the cemetery in Sutton Road, Maidstone, and close to the farm to which the firm had been engaged in carting manure on the night of the boiler explosion on December 3, 1880.

No railway line ran close enough to the quarries to provide a rail connection and though there was a considerable road-borne trade and some carried by barge from Sufferance Wharf, this latter involved a road journey from the quarry to the wharf. Had the quarries been served by a railway connected to the general rail system there is no doubt that the chance of expanding the output would have been enhanced. Though the coated macadam trade had only recently taken its first hesitant steps there is reason to suppose that a railway would have helped the Boughton quarries to join in it as during its first twenty-five years a heavy proportion of the coated macadam tonnage was rail-borne. Certainly this seems to have been the belief of Jesse Ellis.

Having despaired of interesting the South Eastern Railway in promoting a line that would pass near Boughton he had his hopes rekindled by the passage of the Light Railway Act, 1896, under the terms of which so-called "light railways", promoted to serve purely local needs, were relieved of many of the legislative burdens carried by the main line railways and their branches. Foremost of these was the abolition of the need to obtain a private Act of Parliament to authorise their construction, for which was substituted a procedure of approval by order of a body set up for the purpose under the title of *The Light Railway Commission.* This saved large legal fees. Other reliefs were in standards of construction and signalling and in the granting of the concession that each route mile could be charged as a mile and a quarter in calculating passenger and freight rates.

One consequence of this Act was the formation of a company known as The Light Railway Syndicate in which the Engineer and driving force was Holman Fred Stephens. Stephens and his associates were responsible for the Kent & East Sussex Light Railway from Robertsbridge (on the London to Hastings main line) to Rolvenden (1900) and Tenterden (1903). The line was intended to continue to Headcorn, on the London to Ashford line, which it ultimately reached in 1905 and a further company was promoted to build on from there to Maidstone.

It was the latter line, the Headcorn & Maidstone Junction Light Railway, of which Jesse Ellis became one of the promoters in association with Sir Robert Filmer of East Sutton Park, an estate of about 6 700 acres close to Sutton Valence, James Wood and, of course, H.F.Stephens. The most formidable physical obstacle to the progress of the railway was the escarpment at Sutton Valence. The intended route crossed the undulating ground between Headcorn and the foot of the escarpment. Sutton Valence station would have been at the foot of the hill and the route would have climbed it obliquely in the direction of Boughton Monchelsea, after which it levelled out and then fell toward an end-on junction with one of the South Eastern Railway's goods sidings at Tovil. Running powers would have been sought from that point into Maidstone West Station. By this means the light railway would have reached a point not far from the centre of Maidstone yet would have avoided the cost of its own bridge over the River Medway.

The scheme for the line had a prolonged period of gestation but was finally authorised on May 10, 1906. However, despite some of the land for it having been bought, it was never built. The promoters were simply unable to find the capital necessary to do so, though it took many years for them to admit it. As far as is known this was Jesse Ellis's only incursion into railway promotion.

Because it was so long in the process of finding a workable route and obtaining authority to build local people became somewhat impatient. A number of the advocates of a better link between Sutton Valence and Maidstone - Sir Robert Filmer, James Wood, W.S.Forster, W.R.Ward and Jesse Boorman - banded together to produce some more immediate result. The outcome of their endeavours was the setting up of the Sutton Valence & Maidstone Motor Omnibus Co.Ltd. Jesse Ellis was not in this venture but, ever the opportunist, in anticipation of their custom he embarked on the design and manufacture of the steam bus of which a brief mention has already appeared.

In the mechanical parts and chassis it conformed to the pattern of the double framed wagons but had a watertube boiler and amended gear ratios to raise the travelling speeds to 5 and 10 m.p.h. for slow and fast speeds respectively. This latter change turned out to be a mistake as it acquired the reputation of being a most reluctant hill-climber. When exactly it was built is not known but it was ready for the Royal Show in July, 1904.

It was fitted with a handsome hardwood body in two compartments, the rearmost of which, for ladies and non-smokers, carried twelve people on upholstered seats. It was fitted with side windows but only a sliding canvas curtain at the rear. The leading compartment, separated from the rear one by a glazed partition and from the cab by a fixed division, seated eight on two facing cross seats of hardwood slats. This was for smokers and had open sides, closed in by a pair of canvas sliding curtains each side in times when the weather was bad. Fixed steps were provided on each side of this compartment and at the rear to give access to the ladies' compartment. The roof was stiffened and provided with luggage rails and a vertical rear ladder to enable goods or baggage to be carried on top.

The body was a good deal more elaborate than anything attempted at Invicta Works and was most probably supplied by an outside coachbuilder, though the loss of all the Company's records makes it impossible to say whom. However, John Clayton Beadle, who owned shares in the company, was a coach builder in Dartford and it would have been a natural thing for the firm to have turned to him to build the bus body.

The bus underwent some subsequent minor modifications. A late photograph shows the smokers' compartment glassed-in on the offside and the steps removed whilst Stagg & Robson composite wheels appear to have been substituted for the original set, but the wheel change may have been only temporary and for the benefit of publicity activities.

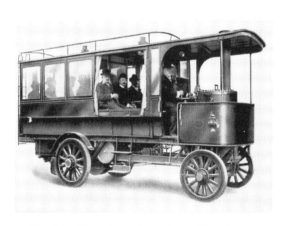

Fig 56: The steam bus plus directors, Jesse (driving), Frank Beadle, and Walter Wilcox (beside him).

Sadly the bus seems to have been a total failure. It was photographed with its maker in the driving seat and other directors including Frank Beadle with the magnificent Dundreary whiskers, in the smokers' area but it never turned a wheel in revenue service and could not find a purchaser. It was still in stock at the beginning of the Receivership, could not be sold in the sale at a figure satisfactory to the Receiver and was eventually sold in 1910, split into two parts, the body to W.A.Stevens for £10.0.0. and the chassis to J.Allen for £60.0.0. on July 9 and 10 respectively. The debit side of the Receiver's report for 1910 contained an item of £9.15.0 paid to Jesse Ellis & Co, supposedly at Allington Forge, for costs concerning this bus, almost certainly for dividing it into the two parts in which it was sold.

As a matter of interest, when the Sutton Valence bus company eventually started its services in October, 1904, it used a 16BHP Clarkson steam single decker with seats for fifteen, soon followed by a similar bus with nineteen seats. The service was shortlived and the buses were offered for sale in the *Commercial Motor* for April 11, 1907, by Messrs Bracher, the Maidstone firm of solicitors, of 33 Earl Street, Maidstone. Where they went is not known - Harrogate has been suggested.

Chapter 13

TRACTION ENGINES and ROLLERS

During the course of his business life Jesse Ellis owned about forty traction engines, road locomotives and road rollers. In considering them below they have been looked at generally in the sequence of the numbers by which they were identified in the fleet list of the limited company. Deviations from this are dealt with as the narrative progresses but it must be borne in mind that it is possible that there may have been some other engines owned by him but sold before the systematic numbering was commenced. All the engines were of Aveling & Porter manufacture unless noted to the contrary.

The engine that had pride of place as No.1 in the Ellis fleet was works No.721, an 8NHP agricultural engine delivered on October 31, 1871, to William Rowe of Linton, near Maidstone, from whom it passed to Jesse Ellis. It was still with the firm when it closed and was bought at the sale by the late Herbie Naylor of Maidstone. Miraculously it survived in his yard in Fant Road until it was bought by the Road Locomotive Society, cosmetically restored by Aveling Barford Ltd. at Grantham and lodged in the Science Museum, Kensington, in 1953.

Engine No.2, a 6NHP agricultural engine which the firm had new from the makers, carried the works No.1099. It was not in the final sale and may be taken as scrapped before that date. Immediately following it came the first pair of Aveling ploughing engines, Nos.1190 and 1191, of 8NHP, which were dispatched on April 4, 1876. Despite the fact that they were still on the strength at the time of the closure sale, at which A.Kemsley, of nearby Aylesford, bought them, they had probably turned out to be a little underpowered for the work their owner expected them to do as the pair he had the next year, Nos.1299 and 1300 (March 2, 1877), were much larger, being 11inches in the bore as compared with 9inches in the earlier pair and classified 14NHP. At the sale Frank Beadle of Herne, Kent, became their new owner, followed by the Wingham Engineering Co. Ltd. who were the owners at the time of their first registration as KE3170 and KE3171. The two sets of ploughers were most likely to have been Nos.3, 4, 5 and 6 in the fleet list.

The next engine bought was gone from the fleet before numbers were allocated. This was works No.1302 (July 5, 1877), an 8NHP road engine provided with two speeds. It was this engine that is thought to have been the one that exploded in Mill Street, Maidstone. According to Lou Humphrey it was rebuilt after the accident and sold. Lou recalled the buyer's name as George Bennett but, on balance, I think it more likely to have been George Barnett of Frindsbury, a few miles away. George Bennett, as we have noticed earlier, was the foreman driver who afterwards went with Jesse Ellis to Allington. Though it would have been fleet No.7, it never carried that number which was actually bestowed upon works No.1661 (March 10, 1881). This latter engine, another agricultural, was not a standard machine. According to its works record sheet it contained parts of No.131, a 10NHP single going back to 1864. The cylinder bore on No.1661 was 9¼inches, against the standard diameter of 9inches, thereby suggesting an old block rebored, yet No.131 had been a 10NHP engine which would have had a 10inch bore cylinder. Notwithstanding its questionable parentage the engine remained with the firm until the end, and probably went to Allington.

The one which followed it in the list, No.8 (works No.238), likewise an 8NHP agricultural engine, was the veteran of the stable going back to January 26, 1867. It may well have been the first engine Jesse Ellis had. Its purchaser when new was William Gardner (or Gardiner) of Milstead. How it came to Ellis is not really known. A good many of his second-hand acquisitions came via Aveling & Porter, being either traded-in or repossessed which may have been how they came to have No.238. It,also, lasted until the closure sale. Fleet No.9 had an uneventful record. Bought new on March 27, 1879, as an 8NHP agricultural engine (works No.1509) it was still working for the firm at the time of the winding-up.

No.10, thought to date from the same year, 1879, did not arrive in the Ellis ranks until nine years later, having served the Vestry of Hampstead, London, in the intervening period. This had the works No.1501. It was a 10-ton roller of the maker's standard design and came to Ellis via Aveling & Porter on October 6, 1888, a year that acquired more general significance by being that during which County Councils came into existence and Jesse Ellis embarked on a serious scale upon the contracting for road works which was both to build up his fortunes and, later, by its loss, destroy them. The roller remained with him until the firm closed. Nos.8,9,and 10 are thought likely to have migrated to Jesse's new venture.

Next in the numerical sequence were his third and last pair of ploughers, 11 and 12, bought on February 16, 1880, with works Nos.1511 and 1512, of 12NHP. These, too, were disposed of in the Receiver's sale and are presumed to have been the pair Jesse Ellis bought for his final venture in partnership with Richard Crosby at Allington. The year 1880 turned out to be one of the pivotal points of Jesse Ellis's career for the boiler explosion in December not only changed his habits of thought but also tied up his financial resources for the next eighteen months or so. In addition it was the first complete year of full-blown agricultural depression. Subsequently he bought only one further agricultural engine, concentrating instead upon the makers' road locomotives.

Of these latter his first purchases after 1880 were the two 8NHP engines that carried the numbers 14 and 15. These were works No.1786 (August 28, 1882) and No.1810 (October 25, 1882). The second of these had a smokebox crane. The two of them were very active in his heavy haulage activities until displaced by the two compound road locomotives *Polly* and *May* in the new century. Even so they continued in the fleet and were sold in October,1907. Thomas Gambrill of Petham, Kent, bought No.14 and No.15 was bought by W.Ovenden of Sittingbourne. Another similar engine was No.19 (works No.1924 of May 19, 1884), sold at the sale and last heard of in the hands of E.A.Foley, the engine dealer of Bourne, Lincs. In October, 1886, perhaps signifying that the agricultural business, though of lesser importance, was not dead, the firm bought an 8NHP convertible agricultural traction engine (works No.2187). This, too, went to E.A.Foley at the sale. It had carried the number 23 at Jesse Ellis & Co.

In looking at these we have departed from the numerical sequence. The engine which was No.17 began life as an 8NHP agricultural engine on January 15, 1883, with the works No.1827, for W.Clinch of Capel, Kent. It was back in the hands of its builders six years later and as the demand for agricultural engines was still at a low ebb it was converted into a 15-ton roller before being sold to Jesse Ellis in June. It was not unique in this transformation. The Eddison Steam Rolling Co's No.136 (A & P No.1836) underwent a similar change. As rollers they were long and heavy - far more in practice than their nominal weight - but also very powerful. When the Ellis stock was sold No.17 had a spell with a short-lived concern known as the Zadig Co. at Southend-on-Sea, Essex, before entering the fleet of W.G.Smoothey & Sons of near-by Rochford. Its stablemate, No.18, was also a 15-ton roller, though built as such under the works No.1640 for Folkestone Corporation, who took delivery on December 19, 1880. It was, therefore, not so powerful as its immediate forerunner in the fleet. Despite both engines being described as 15-tonners the former had a 9inch bore cylinder whilst in the latter it was only 8inches. Jesse Ellis had it by way of Aveling & Porter in October, 1890, and after the sale it became part of the hire fleet of E.A.Foley.

Engine No.20 (works No.1395) was a standard 10-ton roller new to Cheltenham Corporation on November 14, 1877. It arrived at Invicta Works c.1890, and was sold in the sale, doubtless to Ellis and Crosby. The next roller in the list, works No.1162 (December 12, 1877) was new to William de C.Baker of Canterbury. This may well have been fleet No.21 but evidence is lacking. In every respect it is a coy machine. The date when Ellis bought it is uncertain as is that when he sold it to Finn & Co. of Canterbury from whom it finally went for scrap.

The twenty-fourth engine in the list was another 15-ton roller (No.2116, November 25, 1885) bought new by St.George's Vestry, Hanover Square, London, which was subsequently part of the area administered by Westminster City Council. The makers took it back in part-exchange for a new roller and sold it on to Jesse Ellis & Co. The exact date of the transaction is not known but it was probably prior to 1895 as it was one of the rollers used on the reconstruction of the Embankment roadway in that year. It was in the sale in October, 1907, and not subsequently heard of. There are no known candidates for numbers 25 and 26 but 27 was an 8NHP crane engine (No.2670, June 25, 1890). At the October, 1907 sale it was bought by R.M.Packham of Rodmersham, Kent, and last heard of for sale in October, 1946. It then had the registration mark KE2461.

Engine No.28 was a 10NHP road engine (No.527 of February 28, 1870). Originally built for a customer at Swanscombe, Kent, it returned to the hands of the builders and was sold to Jesse Ellis somewhen in the later nineties. It was still there when the firm closed and was bought at the sale by Charles Rouse of Chart Sutton, Kent. The engine immediately following in the fleet order (No.29, works No.1732 of May 2, 1882) was also a road engine, but of 8NHP. It began life with Sir Tatton Sykes, owner of an estate of 34 000 acres at Sledmere, near Malton, Yorks. After him it was owned by J.S.Ward of Nafferton, Yorks. In March, 1899, it was back at its birthplace, Rochester, and was sold almost at once to Jesse Ellis. What happened to it is not known.

The next four numbers in the list (30, 31, 32 and 33) all belonged to rollers bought second-hand from Aveling & Porter. They were, respectively, works numbers 1540 (March 9, 1880), 1922 (November 8, 1883), 1508 (May 5, 1879) and 2792 (February 5, 1891). All were single cylindered except 2792 which began life as an 8NHP compound agricultural engine with W.Bailey at Charlton, near Dover, being converted to a 12-ton roller before being sold by Aveling & Porter to Jesse Ellis. At the sale it was bought by Frank Allchin of Sittingbourne, an engine and machinery dealer, who sold it to L.B.Faulkner of Linslade, Bucks. It was numbered BH8518 in 1921. The other three were all built as rollers. The first of them (No.1540) was new to Coles & Matthews of Coventry, the next to Twickenham Local Board,Middlesex, and the third to the Vestry of St.Matthews, Bethnal Green, London. They all came into Ellis hands in the first half of the nineties and survived until the final sale. No1540 became the property of G.Gregg & Sons of Larne, the destination of the others probably being the new firm at Allington. This was certainly the case with No.31 which appears in a photograph taken there.

Number 34 was a curious acquisition, an 8NHP agricultural engine, No.165, delivered on November 23, 1865, to R.Ward of Egham, Surrey, from whom it moved subsequently to the ownership of Harry Pye at Hoo St.Mary, Kent. From the Pyes it went back to Avelings and Jesse Ellis became its last owner in May, 1894, supposedly for a fairly nominal sum. It was not sold in the sale and must be presumed to have been scrapped prior to that event.

There followed five rollers, all relatively elderly when taken in, at least by the standards of those days. They carried the works numbers 1414, 610, 1404, 1410 and 1462, their respective dates of delivery being February 11, 1878; January 20, 1871; November 11, 1877; January 14, 1878, and September 30, 1878. No.1414 was new to Wolverhampton Corporation and did not arrive in the Ellis fleet until November, 1900. No.610 went first to the Vestry of St.Marylebone, London, and to Ellis in December, 1895. As it was of the Batho type one is tempted to wonder what use he can have made of it, and, indeed, how long it remained in service. Certainly it did not appear in the dispersal sale. Both 1404 and 1410, which he obtained from Avelings in October, 1897, were 10-tonners originally fitted with the conical front rolls and central pivot shaft used by Aveling & Porter at the time they were built. Rollers of this type appear in the picture of the reconstruction of the Embankment roadway in 1895 without any certainty as to their identity. Only Nos.35 (A & P No.1414) and 38 (A & P No.1410) were still with the firm at the date of the sale and are thought to have gone to Allington.

The final roller to be noticed bore the fleet number 39. This was another 15-tonner, No.1462, originally delivered on September 30, 1878, to Littleborough Local Board in Lancashire. How it reached the Ellis fleet or when is not altogether clear. Alan Duke's investigations suggest that it may have arrived in 1898 by way of Burrells. It left at the sale where it was bought by the late Thomas T.Boughton of Amersham Common for whom it ran for many years, after 1921 as BH8408. John Boughton remembers it well from his boyhood and comments that it was known by the nickname of *Copper Top*. Like most rollers of its period it was single speed and the steering chains coiled on separate bobbins outside the brackets.

The last of this catalogue of second-hand purchases was another crane engine, works No.1982 of July 24, 1884, fleet number 40. For some two years or so it was owned by Lord Egerton of Tatton Park, near Knutsford, Cheshire. His Lordship was a noted breeder of shire horses and fond of agriculture. As he owned something in excess of 25,000 acres he had tolerable scope for practising his hobbies. The crane engine soon found itself in a more exacting situation with J.Harvey & Co Ltd. of Hayle, Cornwall, until 1897. In early 1898, it moved to G.Harris & Sons of Privett, Hants, and finally in 1901 to Jesse Ellis & Co.Ltd. It was purchased by Jesse in the 1907 sale for his business at Allington. The number 41 seems likely to have been carried by the 6NHP road locomotive, works No.2773, briefly owned by Jesse Ellis & Co. Delivered on January 1, 1891, it had at least seven other successive owners and had gone from Invicta Works well before the sale.

The numbers 13,16,22,25, and 26 were probably those of the three portable or semi-portable engines owned by the company, the tram engine and the rail-mounted steam crane. Which machine carried which number, however, is not known.

By about the turn of the century Jesse Ellis was at the peak of his prosperity and felt able to resume the purchase of new road engines. The two that he bought were 8NHP compounds bearing the works numbers 4555 (July 10, 1900) and 4665 (January 14, 1901). The former he called *Polly* after the nickname of his wife, Mary, and the second became *May* after his youngest daughter who later became his personal secretary and amanuensis. These two engines became 42 and 43 in the fleet list. Reputedly the Managing Director drove them home himself. For over a decade the increments of the Ellis fleet had been other people's cast-offs. With these he was able once again to stand with pride by the engines for the official photographs.

The seven years left to his company was a short time during which to enjoy them before both were sold in October, 1907. W.Birch of Tilmanstone, near Canterbury, had No.4555 but it changed hands again in 1915 and the third owner was W.Ovenden of Sittingbourne, in whose ownership it became KE2111. The other went to Luke Terry & Sons of Offham near West Malling,Kent, farmers who had enlarged their activities to take in quarrying and agricultural contracting. Whilst with them it was registered as KE4174. Its final owners were Clark Bros. of Bilsington near Ashford, Kent who used it for threshing.

Other engines may well have passed through Ellis hands over the years as few people in his position were able to resist buying and selling when a bargain presented itself but it is believed that these discussed above represent all those used in the business.

The livery of the Ellis engines was green. Mrs.White descibed it as darkish. Charles Hooker reckoned it was more or less the standard works green of Aveling & Porter with maroon front forks on the rollers. Though Charles was grudging in according approval to anything Jesse Ellis had done he conceded that when he knew the Ellis engines the standard of maintenance was good. He probably became familiar with them about a decade after the explosion in Mill Street, which had reflected no glory at all upon the firm's methods, and his observation suggests, as has been remarked elsewhere in the book, that the lessons of the accident had been taken to heart.

During the 1907-1910 partnership the Fowler ploughing engine No.3122 (of 1877) was bought. At one time the property of W.Johnson of Swindon, after the sale this belonged to W.Nocton of Langham, Sussex. How it was used remains enigmatic unless one of the Aveling ploughers had developed a disabling defect.

At the 1907 sale the partners had also bought a four-wheeled tipper steam wagon, the identity of which is discussed in Chapter 10. It was bought by Fremlin Brothers for spares when the rolling stock came to be sold on September 21, 1910. So far as I can trace, it was never registered to run on the road and must have been a white elephant at Allington.

Chapter 14

SOME CONSTRUCTIONAL DETAILS

Whilst it has proved to have been impossible to obtain any particulars of the dimensions of vehicles prior to the first 5-ton double framed wagons information on the latter and its successors is more readily come by. The earlier double framed wagons incorporated the first design of watertube boiler. This, in common with all subsequent boilers on Ellis wagons, worked at 200psi.,having been hydraulically tested after manufacture to 400psi. and was said by *The Engineer* to have had a total heating surface of 75 square feet but not much else is known.

However, a reasonably complete set of leading particulars of the succeeding Ellis-Balmforth firetube boiler for wagons of this type is given by A.J.Wallis Tayler in his "Motor Vehicles for Business Purposes". It has the hallmarks of being based on data from the manufacturers and seems, therefore, likely to be correct. The boiler was described as being of mild steel throughout, the shell plates ½inch thick, the firebox seven-sixteenths inch and the tubeplates ½inch. There were 119 solid cold-drawn steel tubes, 1⅛inch external diameter with ⅛inch thick wall. The total heating surface was 90 square feet, the grate area 3½ square feet. Working pressure was 200psi. and the hydraulic test pressure was 400psi. These and all other Ellis boilers were built to the rules of the National Boiler Insurance Company and the purchase price of a wagon included one year's boiler insurance with that company. The steam, on leaving the boiler proper, passed through a double drying coil in the smokebox. Though a step in the right direction it was not sufficiently effective in imparting superheat to the steam to prevent it arriving wet at the engine. Firing was by a tapered central chute tube. The chimney, situated in front of the firing chute, was double skinned. Clinkering off was done through a forward facing clinkering door a little above grate level. The boiler shell could be split horizontally, the outer shell parting at a peripheral flanged joint. At the top the outer dropped over a circle of 43 ¼inch studs in the flanged top of the smokebox tube plate and was secured by nuts. On this boiler there was a mudhole with bridges at manstand level.

The engine on the double framed 5-ton wagon was placed symmetrically on the centre line. The cylinder diameters on a standard wagon were 4inches and 8inches, with a 6inch stroke. These appear to have been used also in the preceding 3-tonners with the first design of watertube boiler. In fact the indications are that no change was made in the engines between the introduction of the double framed wagons in 1900 and the changes made when the 6-tonner was brought out early in 1907. The exception was the first wagon for the Royal Arsenal Cooperative Society which, if correctly recorded, had larger cylinders and, therefore, quite probably would have been a special design all through, since it seems unlikely that the increased cylinder sizes stated for it could have been achieved merely by boring the cylinders oversize. This, after all, is what one would expect. There was no reason to change the engine. The received wisdom of the moment was that wagon engines had to be cross-compound. It took Stephen Alley and his Sentinel designs to break this mould. Beside this, to have used two high pressure cylinders with any of the Ellis boilers would have run them out of steam far too frequently, a fault to which they were vulnerable in any case.

The valve gear was Stephenson link motion, the valves traditional D-valves. The 90° block pattern crankshaft was of 2¼inch material with a flywheel on the offside end. The helical pinion transmitting the power to the countershaft was keyed to the crankshaft. The double helical pinion engaging with that on the crankshaft was keyed onto the countershaft which was 2⅜inches square. On the nearside end of the countershaft was the eccentric driven pump, constantly in drive, a by-pass being combined with the check valve on the boiler to enable water to be returned to the tanks, one of which was below the driver's seat and the other at the rear. The fast and slow speed pinions were arranged to slide on the squared shaft, interlocked to prevent both being engaged simultaneously and with a central neutral position. Changing gear, however, meant dismounting and kneeling down under the wagon in an uncomfortable or, in extreme cases, possibly dangerous position. The driven gears for the two speeds were combined with the differential on the centre of the 3½inch diameter rear axle. There were two flanged steel sleeves over the back axle, one flanged end of each carrying a bevel wheel and the other being bolted to the hub of the road wheel. The wagons were arranged to have road speeds of 3 and 6mph. though the ratios on the steam bus were higher, 5 and 10mph. The compensating gear could be locked. The following is the makers' explanation of the means by which this was accomplished:

> The locking of the compensating gear is by means of a slotted locking collar which is fixed to axle by means of a lince [sic] pin, a steel slotted locking cap is studded to boss of driving wheel, a square pin fastened in position by a thumb nut drops in slot in locking cap and engages slot in locking collar thus making same fast.

I had the assurance of Charles Hooker, from practical experience, that this was *not* a handy arrangement.

Initially the back axles were available with either plain bronze or roller bearings. Latterly roller bearings appear to have been standard. The other bearings were plain phosphor bronze. All the gearing was of machine cut cast steel. In this arrangement of gear drive any flexing of the sub-frame imposed greater or lesser stresses upon the teeth of the spur gearing. For this reason those gears were made in two parts, the toothed rims fastened to the body of the gear by helicoid spring nuts whereby it was possible to renew the ring of gear, in Wallis Tayler's words, by "simply detaching" the rims. It is true that "simply" is a relative term and while the repair required less expenditure of effort than the taking apart of the whole assembly and fixing new gears his choice of phrase has always struck me as a classic illustration of the saying that nothing makes a job so simple as giving it to someone else.

The frames were of mild steel channel put together with turned bolts and nuts in reamered holes. The sub-frame rode directly upon the front axle and between two collars upon each of the turned sleeves on the rear axle. The main frame was carried upon the axles in hornplates with helical springs. In the case of the front axle there was a transverse leaf spring pivotted at the centre of the front cross member and connected by hangers each end of the front axle. It was intended that this should act as a damper to the more extreme movements of the axle.

The foot brake pedal actuated a band brake on the engine flywheel. The handbrake was by way of a hanging brake beam across the rear bringing two long brake blocks to bear upon the rear tyres. This was operated by a handwheel and quick thread screw. The throttle valve was worked in the same way, always an awkward arrangement with a compound engine.

All the steam fittings were asbestos packed. Besides the pumps the wagons were fitted with Gresham & Craven injectors, arguably the best available. Lubrication of the cylinders was taken care of by a displacement lubricator on the steam pipe on the engine side of the throttle. A single Klinger, or similar, reflex gauge glass was fitted. An elaborate multitubular feedwater heater and device for promoting circulation within the boiler was patented (No.19424, September 9, 1903) jointly by Jesse Ellis (jun.) on the one hand and J.Kitchen , T.Balmforth and H.C.Brown of Balmforth & Co. on the other, but so far as it has been possible to ascertain it was not actually fitted to any of the wagons sold, though it appeared in the firm's catalogues. The water heater was doubtless aimed at improving the effectiveness of the firetube boiler.

Perhaps sensing the futility of further flogging a seemingly dead horse Jesse Ellis (jun.) had already devised a more sweeping alternative to it in the form of a second design of cross watertubed boiler patented jointly by him and the company on July 31, 1903, (No.16818). In this boiler 126 slightly inclined tubes crossed the firebox which was circular on plan, the tubes being arranged so as to leave a central space for the firing chute. The outer shell split peripherally at a flanged joint about six inches above the clinkering door which itself was just above grate level. To remove the upper outer shell meant taking off the chimney and undoing the nuts around the flange, the firing chute and the chimney. That done it could be lifted clear. The fact that the tubes were both inclined and entering a curved plate must have given the boilermakers problems during manufacture. That they could only be re-expanded by opening the boiler made maintenance that much harder. Access for routine washing out was by way of a bolted cover, facing the driver, secured by eight studs and nuts. This gave access to the top waterside of the firebox.

The changes in layout brought about by the move to single frame construction were outlined in Chapter 10. The engine itself remained as before but was moved to the offside. The first shaft still spanned the whole width of the frame but in two parts joined by an Oldham coupling. The change speed pinions were moved onto the first shaft, engaging with mating pinions on a short countershaft between bearings bracketted at one end to the main chassis member and at the other end to a central longitudinal member. The final drive was just to the nearside of the centre. The differential was on the rear axle arranged as in the double framed type but with the lengths of the hollow sleeves differing.

In an effort to ensure that the teeth of the main drive pinions remained in truth the rear axle was linked by radius rods to the second shaft at the nearside and to a trunnion bracketted to the frame on the offside. This maintained the correct depth of mesh in the final drive. To keep the shafts in parallel and, hence, the gears in truth across the width of the teeth, the builders adopted Stevens' spring bar placed behind the rear axle.

In certain wagons, of which the first equipped with a locomotive boiler is an example, the arrangement appears to have been handed, i.e. the flywheel appears on the nearside. The reason for this has not become apparent.

The details of the locomotive type boilers fitted in the latter wagons have not survived. They were fitted with a dome to assist in the collection of dry steam and were fired by a chute through the firebox crown but such information as the total heating surface, grate area, and number and diameter of tubes remains elusive. Though firing a circular firebox through an aperture in the crown was a sound enough idea used widely the same principal applied to a square or rectangular box never worked well because of the problems of keeping sufficient depth of fuel at the corners. Jesse Ellis dropped the idea in 1906 and the 6 ton wagon shown at the March, 1907 Olympia Show had a firedoor in the conventional position in the boiler front. Of this boiler some of the major statistics *are* recorded. The total heating surface was 70.50 square feet and the grate area was reported to be 2.72 square feet, impossibly small for a wagon of this size. In fact, 4.72 sounds more probable. The boiler had 59 smoke tubes of 1½inch diameter. This gave it about the same amount of heating surface as the first design of firetube boiler which had a total of 70 square feet but a grate area of 4.90 square feet.Whereas the 1907 loco boiler was catering for a wagon intended for a 6 ton payload the earlier boiler went into only a 3 tonner, so clearly the loco boiler was expected to be a much more effective steam generator.

From the emphasis placed upon the use of a steam dome and upon the ampleness of the steam space in the 1907 boiler one may deduce that the makers had been stung by complaints about the wetness of steam at the engine. Two other points in the press hand-out have significance. The first was the stress laid upon the use of 3% nickel steel in the gearing of the 6-tonner suggesting that, despite the presence of the spring bar, breakage of gear teeth had been a continuing problem in the single frame wagons. The second was the prominence given to the use of epicyclic gears in the 1907 2-tonner and already referred to in Chapter 10. It is a pity that no details seem to survive of how the engine, gearbox and final drive were arranged nor of the engine dimensions.

Whatever the way in which they may have been laid out the wagon itself must have been a practical worker as is established by its subsequent history. Although the original purchasers kept it only a short time the fact that W.Arnold & Sons, its second owners, kept it going for eleven years does have significance. They were eminently practical people with a large fleet of reliable makes of steam vehicles, maintained in well equipped workshops and expected to work hard. Had the little wagon not fitted into this background it would soon have been discarded.

The hindsight that enables critics to be wondrously wise reveals the Ellis wagons as an intriguing mixture of visionary design and conservatism. The engine itself, a well-made conventional unit, was, in essence, a type that existed in thousands. Other makers were to learn from the experience of Ellis and his contemporaries that double high pressure engines were more compatible with good performance in undertype wagons than were compounds, but the received wisdom during the time he was building was that compounds made for greater thermal efficiency, in appropriate situations, and less exhaust noise. Besides this they learned, albeit hesitantly, from results obtained by Jesse and other pioneers that effective superheat was needed if wagons were not to be wet runners, but in his time superheating was still feeling its way. It was known to produce problems with cylinder lubricants and to lead to scoring of slide valves and port faces. Very soon oils were developed that could stand superheat temperatures and the effect on slide valves was circumvented by the employment of piston valves or cam operated poppet valves. The engine of an Ellis wagon was totally enclosed and lubricated by splashing from an oil sump below the big ends - a good point - but, on the other hand, the expensive train of change speed gears, final drive and differential was open to dust and mud and capable of lubrication only by an awkward crawl under the wagon on the part of the driver.

In refusing to use roller chains Jesse Ellis could, perhaps, be accused of riding a hobby horse. At the time that he began building wagons his aversion had sound foundations for roller chains were a very unreliable commodity for propelling a heavy vehicle as Foden had found, to their cost, in the 1901 War Office Trials. It was said by some that final drive by roller chain was noisy. As compared with a final drive by shaft to a live back axle this was true but against drive by an open chain of gears not so. A practical test of this which could, with application, still be made today, is to compare the sound emission of a Tasker gear driven steam tractor with its chain driven equivalent. Contrariwise, of course, it can again be reasoned that even the most convinced protagonists of the chain, such as Scammell, ultimately had to yield, though that change was then over thirty years in the future. It seems to me, however, that double roller chains from a countershaft containing the differential using more reliable types developed by both Renold and Coventry by about 1906 would have solved his problems of keeping the final drive in truth.

The other thought that is tantalising is why, when so committed to a final drive free of chains, the Ellises did not consider, or, if they considered it, did not develop an engine and gear arrangement with longitudinal shafts and a final drive by prop shaft. There is, of course, absolutely no way of answering such hypothetical questions as all those involved are long dead. My own opinion is that they may well have considered the shaft drives in use up to that time to be too insubstantial to merit trial in a heavy vehicle.

Early tipping wagons had a manually worked tipping gear but in 1904 the firm began to offer a powered version driven from a bevel gear on the flywheel which engaged with a bevel pinion on a short inclined shaft, at the other end of which a worm drove the pinion of the tipping gear. The end of the shaft was keyed so that the bevel pinion could slide along it, the pinion having a collar that engaged with a selector fork actuated by a quick thread screw in the bottom carrying bracket that enabled the bevels to be put into or out of drive with each other. Wagons believed to have had this gear were provisional numbers 28, 45, and, perhaps, 40 (see Appendix 1).

Chapter 15

MISCELLANEOUS TOPICS

Jesse Ellis was a character larger than life, a vast ebullient extrovert possessed of a bone-crushing handshake, a booming voice, a laugh that filled the room and a reputation of succeeding in all that he turned his hand to. Because he seemed able invariably not only to promise but to deliver, his powers of salesmanship were formidable. The explosion of the traction engine in Mill Street was the only major reverse he had suffered up to the age of sixty and even that, by imparting the realisation that he was not infallible, profited him.

The routine selling of hop nidgets, agricultural machines, sulphur, guano, or stable manure to his farmer customers he left to his traveller, Robert Elfick, but in the canvassing of work of a larger kind - heavy haulage, road repairs, or, latterly, the supplying of a steam wagon - he relied upon his own personality and connections. These latter were considerable. From his service in the West Kent Yeomanry he had met, and been of help to, many of the younger members of the landowning families of Kent. His activity in Freemasonry and his involvement with both the Bath & West and Royal Agricultural Societies are likely to have provided him with many introductions and gave him, moreover, a background of dependability. Again, his involvement in the lobbying carried out by the Kent Owners' Association and later by the National Association brought him to the notice of members of public bodies and of Parliament. Arthur Boscawen, the member for the Tonbridge constituency, was probably the foremost of his Parliamentary acquaintances. The combination of all these factors made him a figure of weight and substance, despite his refusal to take part in politics.

Many of these people did not advance his business career directly, but it was useful to him that in the event of his name being mentioned in their presence it should be taken up with approbation rather than with indifference or displeasure.

Another valuable acquaintance who had become a shareholder in the company was Walter Henry Willcox, founder of the firm of oil suppliers and engineers merchants, W.H.Willcox & Co. Ltd, at 23 Southwark Street, Borough, on the doorstep almost of the brewery of Barclay, Perkins & Co. All brewers had steam engines and Willcox supplied many of them with oils, gland packings, pipe jointing and the sundry items that kept their millwrights' departments working. This brewery connection was further enhanced by the fact that Jesse Ellis's business partner - later fellow shareholder - was herself connected with a prominent brewing family. Of the forty-five vehicles thought to have been made by the firm (see Appendix 1) over a quarter were supplied to brewers.

In common with most other manufacturers he cultivated journalists, not only those of the local newspapers of Maidstone, but also of the agricultural and motoring press. From the time the 5-tonners were launched in 1902, he used generous sized, usually half-page or larger, advertisements in the *Agricultural Engineer* and in the *Implement & Machinery Review* illustrating, as a rule, the most recent wagon to have been sold. It is to be feared that sometimes in his rush to give a new order prominence in an advertisement he had the latest client's name written quickly onto any wagon in stock. He seems to have done this in the case of the locomotive boilered wagon (D 1803) supplied to Charrington & Co for their Gravesend depot. A photograph exists of a vertical boilered wagon lettered in their name and carrying that registration mark. By a quirk of chance, or carelessness, this was not used in an advertisement until January 3, 1907, eight months after one showing the actual locomotive boilered wagon supplied, complete with the same registration number!

Though Jesse's friendship with the members of the trade press was not entirely without ulterior motive, in organising such outings as the demonstration over Detling Hill to Sittingbourne (see Chapter 9) he really did have legitimate cause for satisfaction and something of importance to show them. Detling Hill was a killer for heavy horses and presented a severe test for motor lorries as late as the 1930's. For his loaded demonstrator to have traversed it without incident in both directions in one day was, therefore, a very real item of news and not a mere publicity stunt.

The correspondence columns of the trade journals were also used to keep the Ellis name displayed whenever the chance arose. On May 5, 1906, Jesse Ellis (jun.) wrote to the Editor of the *Commercial Motor* :-

> Sir:- In the hope that it may be of interest to your readers, I am sending you this account of a novel trip we did with one of our motor wagons.
>
> We were approached by a gentleman who breeds trout to know if we would undertake to carry some live trout for him to Lurgashall, in Sussex. He had been in the habit of sending them by rail, but owing to the time taken in transit the percentage of fish killed was very great. We promised to do our best for him, and a 5-ton motor wagon and trailer were sent to his breeding ponds at Harrietsham, Kent. They started from there at 8p.m. with 40 cans (30 on the wagon and 10 on the trailer), each can containing 25 live trout 8in. long. A keeper was sent with them to look after their welfare, and they arrived at Lurgashall between three and four o'clock, having lost only 14 fish altogether during the entire distance of about 80 miles. Had it not been that the driver was directed to the wrong route they would have reached their destination four or five hours earlier, but, as it was, they were able to do the journey in less time than the railway company.
>
> On a similar journey by rail 50 fish were lost, and, on one to North Wales, 150 were lost out of 500.
>
> We are expecting to do another journey to the same district very shortly.-
>
> Yours faithfully,
>
> JESSE ELLIS & CO.,LIMITED
>
> Jesse Ellis, Jun., Works Manager.
>
> St.Peter Street, Maidstone.

Whether this promising connection or the firm itself ended first is not recorded.

When Appendix 1 giving the list of wagons built is studied it becomes apparent that if one takes out the seven wagons built for export thirty-one out of the remaining thirty-eight wagons were sold within a twenty-five mile radius of the works. The seven exceptions were the double-framed chassis of the bus which went to John Allen, the double framed wagon for Johnsons Iron & Steel Co. of West Bromwich, the single-framed wagon (D 4411) sold to Samuel Atherton of Shrewsbury, the similar wagons that went to W.Miller of Coventry (D 2270) and to Richardson & Co., Durham (D 2979), and the locomotive boilered wagon (D 5058) sold to Gilson & Son in Somerset by the Receiver.

It must, I believe, be inferred from this that personal selling was more effective than reliance upon printed advertising. It is ,of course, very difficult to suggest whether the export orders arose from wagons being seen at shows and exhibitions, from personal recommendation to a London agent or from more nebulous causes such as Jesse Ellis' masonic connections. Indeed it may be that a combination of these factors came into play.

The fact that the wagons were shown assiduously at both agricultural and commercial vehicle shows aided them in gaining notice in the editorial pages of trade periodicals, helped , no doubt, by Jesse Ellis having been generous, as was his wont, with the whisky or lavish with lunches. Quite a lot of the firm's money must have gone towards achieving this sort of attention creating an overhead that the level of production was not really capable of sustaining. It all savoured a little of whistling loudly in the dark in order to keep the spooks away.

In all general business matters the Ellis firm was progressive. It was one of the first in Maidstone to use the typewriter and was a pioneer of the use of the telephone, having the number Maidstone 2. Telegrams were at the peak of their use around the turn of the century and telegraphic codes flourished. The company used both the ABC 5th Edition and a private code of their own in which standard questions and answers thought likely to be exchanged between the company and its customer were reduced to a series of code words all beginning with the letter 'H'. Jesse Ellis advised all customers to write their telegrams in block letters to avoid errors in transmission by the telegraph operators, a likely happening with ordinary handwriting when the message consisted of a string of apparently unintelligible "non-words". For instance the code word *Habscedens* was to be interpreted as "We cannot supply another wagon same type as last at same price, our price now is :-." One wonders how often this message needed to be transmitted by telegram. Perhaps *Haurementum* had more frequent use. It meant "when was .... supplied; give date and invoice number." On the other hand *Hagolomero*, which stood for "We can fit oil burner to wagon at an additional cost of ...." seems, again, to have a leading position in the rarity stakes. Possibly a more used phrase was *Habutor* - "We cannot agree to your conditions." It is no wonder that the telegraph clerks needed the message in capitals. In all the code words numbered one hundred and sixty-three. How much real advantage can have been gained from the code must be questionable.

So far as the delivery of wagons was concerned, the firm's practice for home orders was to quote "Free-on-Board" at Sufferance Wharf if going by water, or "Free-on-Rail" at Maidstone if despatched by train. Export orders were quoted "Free-on-Board" at the appropriate dock or landing place in London. For home orders the terms of business demanded 25% of the price with the order and the balance on delivery but for export orders the terms were payment in full against Bill of Lading. It was one thing, however, to lay down such conditions but another to enforce them in the competition for orders and probably in practice customers did not all toe these lines.

For test and demonstration runs of wagons the company had three early Kent County Council trade plates, DC 112, 113, and 114. These appear in some of the works photographs of wagons and, as DC is a Middlesborough registration mark, have led to some confusion as to where the wagons were actually registered. Had the pictures been in colour the confusion would not have arisen as it would have been apparent that the plates were lettered in white on a dark red ground instead of the white on black of the contemporary registration plate.

With the exception of one wagon for the Royal Arsenal Cooperative Society, which had a London registration, wagons for home use were registered in Kent. The reason is simple. Many were for Kentish owners in any case and might have been expected to be registered in Kent, but in fact because the interpretations placed upon the vehicle regulations by the various registration authorities were so diverse buyers had been advised by their trade associations and by the technical press to require the makers to register wagons before delivery so that they could be assured that the vehicles would be acceptable under the regulations. Thus the earlier Fodens all had Cheshire registrations, Garretts had the Suffolk mark and Ellis wagons the Kent letter.

There is little doubt that a sizeable section of the local authorities entrusted with vehicle registration used the powers given them as a means of impeding the licensing of steam wagons. Fortunately Kent was not one of these. To this extent Jesse was fortunate in the place where he chose to take up vehicle manufacture and his enterprise began in an atmosphere of goodwill. Even the somewhat testy *Kent Times & Chronicle,* so resolutely opposed to internal combustion vehicles, had given an enthusiastic welcome in its issue of February 18, 1897, to the beginning of the Ellis wagon enterprise as follows:-

MOTOR CARS

We are always pleased to admit when we are wrong, especially about a good thing, and are now pleased to inform our readers that there is, after all, a likelihood of there being a great motor car factory in Maidstone. At any rate Mr.Jesse Ellis is "on the job". In connection with steam power his name is a household word throughout England - we had almost said the wide, wide world - and the oil car being evidently doomed to speedy extinction, steam is now the power most popular with the public, especially with that portion of it having any money to invest in motor cars. Mr.Ellis contemplates converting his present extensive traction engine business into a limited company. and including therewith the manufacture of motor cars, for which purpose he is in negotiation for the purchase of an extensive plot of land adjoining the Invicta Works on the banks of the Medway at Maidstone, where he proposes to erect a factory on a greatly extended scale, and to find employment for many hundreds of workmen. His scheme is, we are glad to hear, being warmly taken up by local and other capitalists, and it is hoped soon to float it under the most favourable auspices. As is well-known, the familiar "Jesse" is a man of great energy, enterprise, and business aptitude; anything he takes in hand generally succeeds. Next week we hope to put our readers in possession of fuller information in relation to this important project.

Possibly Jesse had overstated his ambitions or the reporter had read more than was intended into them but the message was clear. If Jesse had taken it up the enterprise was likely to succeed.

Ten years later the whole edifice was on the verge of ruin. The "factory on a greatly extended scale" had never happened. Jesse, almost for the first time in his life, had backed a hunch that had turned out to be wrong several times over. Firstly, although steam captured a useful section of the heavy vehicle market it never became either supreme or uncontested in it. Indeed, so far as buses were concerned, it hardly survived the first few years. Secondly, British motor manufacturing in general grew at nothing like the predicted pace, encumbered and discredited as its early years were by the debacles surrounding the activities of the nefarious Harry J.Lawson and others intent more on parting investors from their money rather than upon initiating manufacture. In the third place, it seems likely that Jesse Ellis vastly underestimated the cost of developing and marketing a successful vehicle or the amount of technical backing required to do so. Though his basic business was sound in its field it was not in the same class as, for instance, Thornycroft, rooted in naval ship-building, Foden, already makers of high class traction engines, or Sentinel, a prominent name in the making of large valves and small ships. When Kent County Council took the decision to manage by direct labour the 100 miles or so of its roads previously maintained under contract by Ellis & Co, it dealt the firm a dreadful blow. The very part of the enterprise that had been supplying the cash to experiment with steam wagons was suddenly and irrevocably lost. The base upon which the development work had been supported was destroyed.

Though Jesse Ellis had not arrived at a definitive design of wagon by the time the Receivership put an end to his efforts he had, nonetheless, laid down some very sound precepts, amongst which may be enumerated: [i] a chassis assembly using turned bolts in reamered holes; [ii] standardisation of components and work to limit gauges; [iii] the maintenance of a comprehensive stock of spares; [iv] the policy of using only the best materials and components such as, for instance, phosphor bronze bearings, cast steel gears, Klinger gauge glass fittings, Gresham & Craven injectors, and the option of roller bearings to the driving axle. Had he been willing to use a roller chain once a sufficiently strong chain had become available, he would have both cheapened production and eliminated a source of weakness. With the advantage of having seen the end of the story we know that compound engines achieved real success only on overtypes and that the enduringly successful undertypes made use of moderate but effective superheat. The Ellises were still groping toward this realisation when the firm closed. If they could have gone on for a further two or three years they would very likely have taken these points but as it was the opportunity was denied them.

Jesse Ellis was a notable pioneer at the very outset of wagon building when other firms, later to make names in the business, were content to observe from the sidelines how events might develop. He had high ideals of quality and several advanced targets in design. The trials he experienced in putting these into practice were to be useful markers to other builders who came later. Like most pioneers some of the avenues he explored turned out to be dead ends and before he achieved financial success with wagon building his money ran out. We must applaud, therefore, his boldness and vision and commiserate upon his ultimate failure but let us never belittle what he did.

Fig 57: The last Ellis wagon of the Fremlin fleet (Prov.No.41) with driver Wally Cruttenden (r.) and trouncer Bidgood (l.) delivering beer in Maidstone, c.1923.

Bibliography

BOOKS

Beaumont W.Worby	Motor Vehicles and Motors	Constable	1900 etc
Edmeades J.F.	Some Historical Records of the West Kent (Q.O.)		
	Yeomanry 1794 - 1909	Melrose	19(
Glen A.	The Highway, Locomotive & Turnpike Acts	Knight	18.
Hutchinson I.K.	Traction Engine Locomotives	Road Locomotive Society	19!
Norris W.	Modern Steam Road Wagons	Longmans	19!
Wallis Tayler A.J.	Motor Vehicles for Business Purposes	Lockwood	19!
	Maidstone in 1892	Robinson, Son & Pike	18!
	Directory of Maidstone	Kent Messenger	variou
	Directory of Maidstone	Kelly	variou
	Directory of Kent	Kelly	variou
R.A.S.E.	Catalogues of Shows 1897 - 1907	R.A.S.E.	variou
	Abridgements of Patents	H.M.Patent Office	variou

PERIODICALS and REPORTS

Agricultural Engineer
Autocar
Automotor & Horseless Vehicle Journal
Commercial Motor
Engineer
Engineering
Implement & Machinery Review
Kent Messenger

Kent Times & Chronicle
Maidstone Gazette
Motor Car Journal
Motor Traction
South Eastern Gazette
Steaming
The Pictorial Record
World's Carriers

Report, Select Committee of the House of Commons on Traction Engines - 1896

No register of the wagons built by the firm is known to survive nor is it established conclusively that works numbers were allocated to steam wagons in a continuous series. The only direct evidence to support the existence of numbers in a consecutive series is that the two water cart wagons included in the sale of October 1, 1907, were referred to as numbers 27 and 28.

The list of wagons given below, based upon the available evidence, shows that the position of these two wagons in the output is consistent with numbers having been allocated consecutively and not in some arbitrary fashion, i.e. not allocated by some such system as using two numbers and ignoring the next two. Where features of wagons are known for certain to have existed i.e. because they appear in photographs and/or the registration records of local authorities, they are entered in firm type. Where not vouched for from such sources they are in italic type.

References:
IMR; Implement & Machinery Review
Cat; Firm's catalogues

AHV; Automotor & Horseless Vehicle Journal
RSC; Royal Show Catalogues

CM; Commercial Motor
KRR; Kent registration records.

Abbreviations
CBW   Colonial buck wagon
W2   Two ton wagon
W3   Three ton wagon
W5   Five ton wagon [suffix T=tipper]
Boilers
VFT   Vertical Field tube
CWT 1 Crossed watertube - 1st type
CWT 2 Crossed watertube - 2nd type
FT 1 Firetube - 1st type
FT 2 Firetube - 2nd type

WORKS NO.	DATE	TYPE	BOILER	REG.NO.	PURCHASER	REFERENCE	REMARKS
1	1897	CBW	VFT	-	None known	IMR 1.1.98	
2	1898	CBW	VFT	-	None known	(AHV 6.98 (RSC 1898	Cab first
3	1898	CBW	VFT	-	*Dartford Brewery*	RSC 1899	Steered from front
4	1899	W2	De Dion	D442	Fremlin Bros.	RSC 1899	Chain driven, withdrawn 1907
5	*1900*	W2	CWT1	-	Demonstrator	RSC 1900	Double frame
6	1901	W3	CWT1	-	London & Counties	IMR 3.7.01	Double frame
7	1901	W3	CWT1	-	Ditto	IMR 2.8.01	Double frame
8	1901	W3	CWT1	-	Ditto	Ditto	Double frame
9	1901	W3	CWT1	-	Ditto	Ditto	Double frame
10	1901	W3	CWT1	-	Ditto	Ditto	Double frame
11	1901	W3	CWT1	-	Ditto	Ditto	Double frame
12	1901	W3	CWT1	-	Ditto	Ditto	Double frame
13	1902	W3	FT1	-	Egyptian Govt.	Various	Double frame. Desert wheels
14	1903	W3T	FT1	-	Cairo Sanitary Admin.	Various	Double frame. Steel wheels
15	1903	W3	FT1	=	India Developments	Cat	Double frame. Steel wheels
16	1903	W3	FT1	D446	Dartford Brewery Co.	KRR	Double frame
17	1903	W3	FT2	-	Clyde Engineering (Australia)	Cat	Double frame
18	1903	W3	FT2	D337	Style & Winch	KRR	Double frame
19	1903	W3	FT2	D330	J.Batchelor	KRR	Double frame
20	*1903*	*W5*	FT2	A 78	RACS	Cat	Double frame

(contd)

Appendix I (contd)

Works No	Date	Type	Boiler	Reg.No	Purchaser	Reference	Remarks
21	1904	W3	FT2	D974	J.Balmforth & Co.	KRR	Double frame
22	1904	W3	FT1	-	Hammerton & Co.	IMR 1.4.04	Double frame
23	1904	W3	FT2	D1109	Fremlin Bros.	KRR	Double frame
24	1904	W3	FT2	D1196	Johnsons Iron & Steel Co.	KRR	Double frame
25	1904	W3T	FT2	D1250	John Williams & Co.	KRR	Double frame
26	1904	W3T	CWT2	-	Barraud & Abraham	RSC	Double frame
27	1904	W3T	FT2	-	Stock: then to Jesse Ellis & Co, Allington	Sale documents	Double frame. Street watering body. Bought by Fremlins as spares
28	1904	W5T	CWT2	D4411	Stock: then to Samuel Atherton	KRR	Single frame. Ditto, removed before sale by Receiver
29	1904	Bus	CWT2	-	Jesse Ellis & Co	RSC	Double frame. Chassis to J.Allen, 1910
30	1904	W3T	FT2	D1561	Maidstone Corporation	KRR	Double frame
31	1904	W3	FT2	D1551	E.& H.Kelsey	KRR	Double frame
32	1904		CWT2	D1496	Demonstrator: then to Fremlin Bros.	KRR	
33	1904		CWT2	-	Hajee Ismael Sait	KRR	Single frame. Ran until 1920
34	1905	W5	CWT2	D1688	RACS		Single frame
35	1905	W2	*CWT2*	D2393	Demonstrator + experimental: then to: Fremlin Bros.	KRR	Single frame
36	1905	W5	Loco	D1822	Dartford Brewery Co.	KRR	Single frame
37	1905	W5	Loco	D1803	J.Ellis & Co. then to: Charrington & Co	KRR	Single frame
38	1906	W5T	*not certain*	-	Hajee Ismael Sait	CM 27.9.06	Single frame
39	1905	W5	CWT2	D2270	J.Ellis & Co. then to: W.Miller, Coventry	KRR	Single frame
40	1906	W5	CWT2	D2672	P.H.G.Powell-Cotton	KRR	Single frame. Ran until c.1927
41	1906	W5	CWT2	D2891	Fremlin Bros.	KRR	Single frame. Ran until 1927
42	1906	W5	*CWT2*	D2979	Richardson & Co.	KRR	Single frame
43	1907	W2	FT2	D3457	H.Summers & Son	IMR 1.4.07	Single frame. Epicyclic gearbox
44	1907	W6	*Loco*	D5058	S.C.Gilson & Son	KRR	Single frame. Still running 1920
45	1906	W5T	*Loco*	-	Valparaiso	IMR 1.4.07	Single frame. Street watering body
46	1907	*Petrol engined van.*					

APPENDIX II - ORDINARY SHAREHOLDERS in JESSE ELLIS & CO.LTD. 1898
The list is in the order in which the names occur in the statutory return to the Board of Trade.
The figures give the number of £1 ordinary shares held.

Thomas Scott, Ditton,	Farmer	501
Walter Thomas Fremlin, Milgate Park, Maidstone.	Brewer	500
Grace Blackett, (Mrs.) 1 St.Michaels Terrace, Maidstone.	Married woman	15
George Burnett Blackett Ditto	Salesman	10
Ambrose Roberts, Jessamine Cottage, Barming.	Accountant	40
W.H.Willcox & Co.Ltd. 23 Southwark St. London SE	Oil Merchants	200
Walter Henry Willcox, Ditto	Oil Merchant	300
William P.Dickinson, High St. Maidstone.	Printer+Stationer	50
Ralph James Fremlin, Heathfield, Maidstone.	Brewer	3 001
Frank Fremlin, Warden House, Maidstone.	Brewer	1 001
Richard Henry Fremlin, Wateringbury.	Brewer	3 000
William Cable, Teston.	Farm Manager	500
Thomas Reader, Barming.	Farm Bailiff	25
Francis John Beadle, The Oaks, Belvedere.	Merchant	1 501
Richard Thomas Porter, Raleigh, Beckenham.	Engineer	250
Thomas Lake Aveling, Boley Hill Ho. Rochester.	Engineer	250
George Hiram Leavey, 12 New Road Ave.Chatham.	Outfitter	100
Abraham March Flint, Millhall, Larkfield.	Corn+Coal Mercht	250
Robert Batcheller, Highfield, Pembury.	Merchant	250
Robert Stewart, New House, Allington.	Farmer	200
Bertram Noakes, 8 Southwark St. London SE	Hop Factor	300
Charles Francis Hartridge, 146 Leadenhall St.	Ship Owner	250
Fred Beadle, Fairholme, Belvedere.	Coal Merchant	126
John Clayton Beadle, The Oaks, Belvedere.	Coach Builder	125
Herbert Edgar Beadle, Ditto.	Contractor	125
Rosa Jane Beadle, Ditto	Married Woman	100
George Gray, St.Phillips Works, Sheffield.	Manufacturer	50
Frederick James Wain, Mitre Hotel, Maidstone.	Lic. Victualler	50
John Sibley, 22/28 Gabriels Hill, Maidstone	Ironmonger	100
Wm.Henry Duffield, 34 Queen St. London	Architect	50
William Hayman, Rochester.	Importer	25
Jesse Ellis, Invicta Works.	Engineer	1
Percival Johnson Burt, 28+29 St.Swithins Lane,London.	Solicitor	1
Marianne Fremlin, 12 Deans Road, Willesden Green.		9 955
Jesse Ellis, Invicta Works.	Engineer	5 826
Ellis & Fremlin, St Peters Street, Maidstone.	Engine Proprs.	4 012

By 1903 the shareholders included in addition:-

George Bennett, 18 Well St. Maidstone,	Foreman	50
Charles Frederick Ellis, London Rd. Maidstone.	Foreman	50
Edith Amy Wood, Southampton.	Married Woman	85
Minnie Kate Tite, Luxor, Upper Egypt.	Married Woman	85
Jesse Ellis (jun.), Gothic House, Maidstone.	Engineer	75
Arthur Ellis, Famagustra,[sic] Cyprus.	Engineer	75
Mabel Mary Ellis, Kingsgate, London Rd. Maidstone.	Spinster	85
Ethel Daisy Ellis, Ditto	Spinster	115
May Isabel Ellis Ditto	Spinster	130
Douglas Ellis Ditto		150
Richard Denny Crosby, St.Peters Street		52

plus 7 other members of the Fremlin family, including A.G.W.Fremlin (farmer) of Ficksburg, OFS,
S.Africa. Four members had 1 559 each, and three had 1 558 each - a total of 10 910.

APPENDIX III - ENGINES OWNED BY JESSE ELLIS & CO.

All are by Aveling & Porter Ltd. Rochester, and all single cylinder except Nos.42 and 43, (compounds).

Fleet No.	Works No.	Year	Bought	Type	Sold	Previous Owner	Subsequent Owner
1	721	1871	?	8NHP TE	1907	W.Rowe, Linton, Kent	H.Naylor,Maidstone
2	1099	1876	New	6NHP TE	?	--	
3	1191	1876	New	8NHP PE	1907	--	A.Kemsley, Aylesford
4	1190	1876	New	8NHP PE	1907	--	A.Kemsley
5	1299	1877	New	14NHP PE	1907	--	F.Beadle, Herne
6	1300	1877	New	14NHP PE	1907	--	F.Beadle
7	1302	1877	New	8NHP RE	?	--	Exploded in Mill Stree
7	1661	1881	New	8NHP TE	1907	--	*J.E.&Co. Allington*
8	238	1867	?	8NHP TE	1907	W.Gardner	*Ditto*
9	1509	1879	New	8NHP TE	1907	--	*Ditto*
10	1501	1879	1888	10T roll	1907	Vestry of Hampstead	*Ditto*
11	1511	1880	New	12NHP PE	1907	--	*Ditto*
12	1512	1880	New	12NHP PE	1907	--	*Ditto*
13	See below						
14	1786	1882	New	8NHP RE	1907	--	T.H.Gambrill, Petham
15	1810	1882	New	8NHP RE	1907	--	W.Ovenden, Sittingbour
16	See below						
17	1827	1883	By 1889	15T roll	1907	W.Clinch, Capel,Kent	Zadig Co, Southend-on-
18	1640	1880	1890	15T roll	1907	Folkestone Corporation	E.A.Foley, Bourne
19	1924	1884	New	8NHP RE	1907	--	E.A.Foley
20	1395	1877	1885	10T roll	1907	Cheltenham Corporation	*J.E.&Co. Allington*
21	1162	1875	?	15T roll	1907	W.de C.Baker, Canterbury	Finn & Co, Canterbury
22	See below						
23	2187	1886	New	8NHP TE	1907		E.A.Foley
24	2116	1885	?	15T roll	1907	Vestry of St.George)	
25	See below					Hanover Sq. London)	
26	See below						
27	2670	1890	New	8NHP CE	1907		R.M.Packham, Rodmersha
28	527	1870	?	10NHP RE	1907	J.Coveney, Swanscombe	C.Rouse, Chart Sutton
29	1732	1882	1899	8NHP RE		J.S.Ward, Nafferton,Yorks	
30	1540	1880	?	15T roll	1907	Coles&Matthews, Coventry	G.Gregg & Sons. Larne
31	1922	1883	?	15T roll	1907	Twickenham L.B.	*J.E.&Co. Allington*
32	1508	1879	1893	15T roll	1907	Vestry of St.Matthews	*Ditto*
33	2792	1891	?	12T roll	1907	W.Bailey,Charlton, Kent	F.W.Allchin
34	165	1865	1894	8NHP TE		H.Pye, Hoo St.Mary	
35	1414	1878	1900	15T roll	1907	Wolverhampton Corporation	*J.E.&Co. Allington*
36	610	1871	1895	15T roll		Vestry of St.Marylebone	
37	1404	1877	1897	10T roll		Fulham Board of Works	
38	1410	1878	1897	10T roll	1907	Bournemouth Commissioners	*J.E.&Co. Allington*
39	1462	1878	*1898*	15T roll	1907	Littleborough L.B. Lancs	T.T.Boughton&Sons,Amer
40	1982	1884	1901	6NHP CE	1907	G.Harris & Sons, Privett	*J.E.&Co. Allington*
41	2773	1891	?	6NHP RE		W.Hooker, Langley,Kent	
42	4555	1900	New	8NHP RE	1907	--	W.Birch, Tilmanstone
43	4665	1901	New	8NHP RE	1907	--	L.Terry & Sons, Offham

NOTES
Information in italic type in the foregoing list, though probable, is not established beyond doubt.
Fleet Nos.13,16,22,25 and 26 were probably allocated to the three portable or semi-portable engines, the tr
engine and the rail-mounted steam crane.

84

Index